# SPRING HARVEST
## P R A I S E

## GAME**CHANGERS**
## SONGBOOK

## 60 NEW SONGS FOR THE CHURCH
### WITH FULL SCORES

# COPYRIGHT & PHOTOCOPYING

# ACKNOWLEDGEMENTS

Music type-setting for scores and lead sheets: David Ball
Guitar chords: David Ball
Artwork: Sublime | wearesublime.com
Executive Producer: Peter Martin

Special thanks to Brenda Cameron and all at Cambron Software for Power Music and your help in developing this resource.

Spring Harvest wishes to acknowledge and thank the following people for their help in the compilation and production of this songbook: Denise Anstead, Pete Broadbent, Andrew Crookall, Jaqs Graham, Cheryl Jenkinson, Sue Rinaldi & Rachel Whitney.

Published & distributed by Elevation, 14 Horsted Square, Uckfield, East Sussex, TN22 1QG, UK.
An activity of Memralife Group, Registered Charity number 1126997, a Company limited by guarantee, registered in England and Wales, number 6667924. Registered Office: 14 Horsted Square, Uckfield, East Sussex, TN22 1QG.

All Scripture quotations unless indicated otherwise taken from THE HOLY BIBLE, NEW INTERNATIONAL VERSION®, NIV® Copyright © 1973, 1978, 1984, 2011 by Biblica, Inc.® Used by permission. All rights reserved worldwide.

SHM2135B

ISBN 978-1-911237-01-03

# CONTENTS

Discover the Spring Harvest Digital Songbook ..................... 4-5

Alphabetical and Key Index ........................................ 6-8

Songs .............................................................. 10-195

Songs are listed in the order of first line, not title.

Bridges to C ....................................................... 196

Bridges to D ....................................................... 197

Bridges to E ....................................................... 198

Bridges to F ....................................................... 199

Bridges to G ....................................................... 200

Guitar Chords ...................................................... 201-203

Scripture Index .................................................... 204-208

Thematic Index ..................................................... 209-211

# DISCOVER THE SPRING HARVEST DIGITAL SONGBOOK

Over the years of the Spring Harvest Songbook, we have always been looking at how we can use technology to make worship leaders' lives easier and make the flow of worship smoother. Power Music from Cambron Software has been at the heart of our digital songbooks since 2011 and is widely used by worship musicians to free themselves from the hassles of paper music. In Power Music all your music is instantly available on-screen for practice and performance.

Once again we have worked in partnership with Cambron Software to create a digital version of the Spring Harvest 2016 Songbook. This includes sheet music, chord sheets, lyrics and all the indexing required to find your songs quickly.

Use your iPad, PC, laptop, Windows tablet or Mac as a "digital" music stand to display music or chord sheets on-screen.

## WHY USE POWER MUSIC?

- Songs are easy to find by title, first line, category, author and Bible reference

- Quickly set up playlists for your services

- Transpose chord sheets, add capo chords

- Add performance notes

- Link audio tracks for practice or performance.

- Using multiple screens keeps the whole band on the same page

- Synchronised iPad display

- Page turning becomes simple using a foot pedal or by simply tapping a screen or a keyboard.

No more searching for scraps of paper, no more filing song sheets, no more photocopying - Power Music makes worship times stress free for musicians.

## GAME**CHANGERS**
### SONGBOOK

**iPAD**

Get Spring Harvest 2016 Songbook on your iPad using the free Power Music app.

**DOWNLOAD*** (Windows & Mac OS X)

- Display sheet music and chord sheets
- Transpose chord sheets
- Search by title, author, category, Bible reference

Find your unique reference code on the inside front cover

 Windows®  Mac

**HELP***

Getting started

*See inside front cover for details

# ALPHABETICAL INDEX

[Song titles differing from first lines are in italics]

| Key | First Line / Title | No. |
|-----|--------------------|-----|
| | **A** | |
| B | All glory, all honour | 1 |
| B | *Abide with me* | 17 |
| G | *Alive with worship* | 23 |
| Db | *All for you* | 2 |
| C | *All hail King Jesus* | 58 |
| Db | All I am for you, oh Lord | 2 |
| F | *All our hallelujahs* | 25 |
| Eb | *Alleluia, he has loved us* | 50 |
| G | *Arms* | 4 |
| | **B** | |
| A | Before the earth was made you were living | 3 |
| | **C** | |
| A | *Cling to the cross* | 53 |
| | **E** | |
| G | Empty handed here I come | 4 |
| Bb | *Every giant will fall* | 15 |
| A | Every painful day I've known | 5 |
| A | *Everything and nothing less* | 14 |
| G | *Eyes on you* | 26 |
| | **F** | |
| F | *Fascinate* | 31 |
| D | For we trust in our God | 6 |
| Bb | *Forever yours* | 20 |
| Bb | From him, through him, and to him are all things | 7 |
| C | From the breaking of the daylight | 8 |

| Key | First Line / Title | No. |
|-----|--------------------|-----|
| | **G** | |
| D | Go in peace | 9 |
| Bb | *God of miracles* | 27 |
| B | *God with us* | 54 |
| Ab | God, you can tell the waves 'be still' | 10 |
| A | *Good, good father* | 24 |
| G | Grander earth has quaked before | 11 |
| Bb | *Greater* | 7 |
| | **H** | |
| C | *Hallelujah* | 42 |
| D | Hear our cry, oh King of heaven | 12 |
| B | *Held high* | 57 |
| C | *Here with me* | 48 |
| C | *Holy moment* | 41 |
| D | *Honey* | 60 |
| D | *Hope and glory* | 12 |
| G | *How sweet the sound* | 13 |
| G | How sweet the sound of Jesus' name | 13 |
| A | Humbly I stand, an offering | 14 |

| Key | First Line / *Title* | No. |
|-----|----------------------|-----|
| | **I** | |
| A | *I believe* | 5 |
| Bb | I can see the Promised Land | 15 |
| C | I cast my mind to Calvary | 16 |
| B | I have a home | 17 |
| C | I look upon the face | 18 |
| B | I was nowhere | 19 |
| C | *I will hope* | 35 |
| Bb | I will wait on you Lord | 20 |
| E | I'll be the altar | 21 |
| G | Immortal, invisible | 22 |
| D | *In God we trust* | 36 |
| Eb | *In your presence* | 52 |
| G | *It is well* | 11 |
| E | *It is well with my soul* | 34 |
| G | I've come here today to worship again | 23 |
| A | I've heard a thousand stories of what they think you're like | 24 |
| | **J** | |
| F | *Jesus Christ, Emmanuel* | 25 |
| G | Jesus, Jesus, how I trust you | 26 |
| B | *Jesus, the One who saves* | 1 |
| | **K** | |
| A | *King of my heart* | 28 |
| | **L** | |
| E | *Lead me to the rock* | 39 |
| Bb | Let faith arise in spite of what I see | 27 |
| E | *Let me burn* | 21 |
| A | Let the King of my heart | 28 |
| | **M** | |
| G | Mighty in battle, perfect in love | 29 |
| A-B-Db | My soul longs for Jesus | 30 |

| Key | First Line / *Title* | No. |
|-----|----------------------|-----|
| | **N** | |
| F | *Never gonna stop singing* | 56 |
| F | No eye has seen | 31 |
| Bb | *No longer slaves* | 59 |
| G | *Not be moved* | 40 |
| | **O** | |
| D/E | O love that will not let me go | 32 |
| C | *O praise the name (Anastasis)* | 16 |
| A | Our God is a keeper of his word | 33 |
| E | Our scars are a sign | 34 |
| C | Overhead, skies are dark | 35 |
| D | *Overwhelmed but I won't break* | 36 |
| | **P** | |
| C | *Plans* | 8 |
| A | *Pour out* | 33 |
| F# | *Power in the cross* | 44 |
| G | Praise unbroken | 37 |
| D | *Psalm 4* | 49 |
| | **R** | |
| F | *Refuge* | 55 |
| | **S** | |
| Ab | *Songs in the night* | 10 |
| C#m | Spirit of God | 38 |
| E | Standing in this place of tears | 39 |
| | **T** | |
| G | The Lord is our salvation | 40 |
| B | *The way* | 19 |
| C | This is a holy moment | 41 |
| A | *To the highest place* | 3 |
| A | *Touch the sky* | 47 |

| Key | First Line / Title | No. |
|-----|--------------------|-----|
| | **U** | |
| G | *Unbroken praise* | *37* |
| G | *Unto your name* | *29* |
| | **W** | |
| C | Wake up my soul and turn to him | 42 |
| C | Watching, waiting for your fire again | 43 |
| F# | We all stand amazed | 44 |
| D | We are waiting | 45 |
| D | *We will not be shaken* | *6* |
| B | What a Saviour | 46 |
| A | What fortune lies beyond the stars | 47 |
| C | When darkness deepens | 48 |
| D | When I call | 49 |
| Eb | When I was lost | 50 |
| Ab | When my fears are overtaking | 51 |
| Eb | When your Spirit rushes in | 52 |
| A | Where can we go | 53 |
| C | *Wide open spaces* | *18* |
| C | *Wildfire* | *43* |

| Key | First Line / Title | No. |
|-----|--------------------|-----|
| | **Y** | |
| B | You are matchless in grace and mercy | 54 |
| Ab | *You are my peace* | *51* |
| F | You are my refuge | 55 |
| F | You called out | 56 |
| B | You give me a brand new name | 57 |
| C | You sit enthroned in majesty | 58 |
| Bb | You unravel me with a melody | 59 |
| D | Your name is honey on my lips | 60 |

# GAME**CHANGERS**
## SPRING HARVEST 2016

# TOGETHER
WE CAN CHANGE THE WORLD

# ALL GLORY, ALL HONOUR
## [JESUS, THE ONE WHO SAVES]

Key = B

Capo 4 (G)

♩ = 76

Jamie Hill

**Verse**

1. All glo - ry,— all ho - nour— to the One who— saves;—
2. We're seek - ing,— we're long - ing— for the One who— saves—
3. May we see— your glo - ry— in— all you— do?—
4. Can we see— your beau - ty— in— all you— do?—

death beat - en,— sin— bro - ken,—
to bring heal - ing,— do a new thing,—
Eyes - see - ing,— ears— hear - ing—
Our eyes see - ing,— ears— hear - ing—

**1.,3.**
we can ne - ver be— the same.—
hearts— af - ter— you.—

**2.,4.**
re - vive this na - tion— a - gain.—
hearts— af - ter— you.—

**Pre-chorus**
We are see - ing streams— in— the de - sert;

CCLI# 7053430

12

- sert; Lord, we're cry-ing out— for more.— We are see-ing

— Je-sus, the One who— saves.—

**SPRING HARVEST**
**song** search

If you need help to find a song on a particular theme or Scripture passage, or just want to know which of the Spring Harvest songbooks or albums features the song you're after - use our song search.

» search online at **www.springharvest.org/songsearch**

# ALL I AM FOR YOU, OH LORD
## [ALL FOR YOU]

Key = D♭

Capo 4 (A)

Dave Miller

1. All I am for you, Oh Lord, ev-'ry-thing that I a-dore, your
hopes and dreams are yours to change, I free-ly give as you free-ly gave; I sur-

2. My

cross de-mands my life, my all._____ pur-po-ses._____
ren-der to your

All_ for you,_ Je - sus,_ I'll be a fool_ for you,_ Je-

CCLI# 7026930

all I—am, all I have, at your feet, in your hands. All I—am, all I have,

at your feet, in your hands.—

And

# BEFORE THE EARTH WAS MADE YOU WERE LIVING
## [TO THE HIGHEST PLACE]

# 3

Key = A

Rivers & Robots

𝅘𝅥 = 150

1. Be - fore the earth was made you were liv - ing, and o - ver ev - 'ry heart you've been sing - ing. Your ve - ry word spoke life in - to be - ing, you

2. Step - ping down in - to the world you made, the un - cre - a - ted God in a hu - man frame. Cre - a - tor dwel - ling with cre - a - tion, you

e - ven give___ the breath___ we___ are breath - ing.___ And now,___
made your - self___ of no___ re - pu - ta - tion. And you

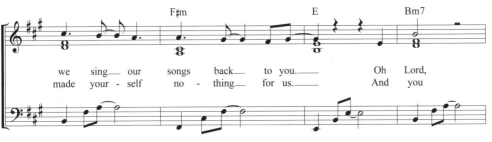

we sing___ our songs back___ to you.___ Oh Lord,
made your - self no - thing___ for us.___ And you

*(v.2)*

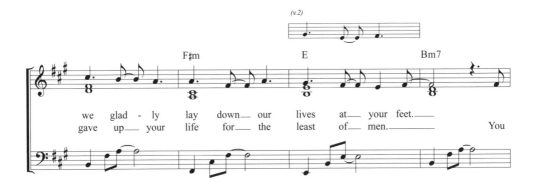

we glad - ly lay down___ our lives at___ your feet.___ You
gave up___ your life for___ the least of___ men.___

We take___ the breath___ you gave, and
en - tered___ the gates___ of death and___

we give— it back———— in praise. 'Cause
rose with— the keys——— in— your hand.——— And now

**Chorus**

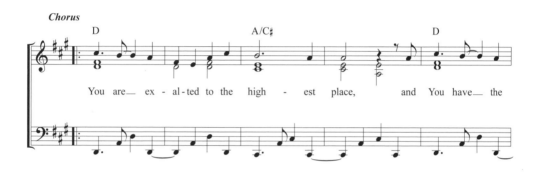

You are— ex - al - ted to the high - est place, and You have— the

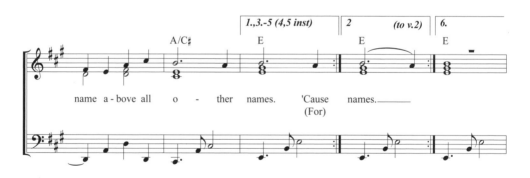

name a - bove all o - ther names. 'Cause names.———
(For)

**Bridge**

*Repeat 6 times (last 2 instrumental)*
*(Fine)*

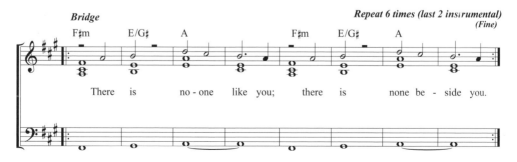

There is no - one like you; there is none be - side you.

**4**

# EMPTY HANDED HERE
# I COME
## [ARMS]

Key = G

Tim Hughes, Martin Smith,
Nick Herbert & Jonas Myrin

♩ = 70

1. Emp-ty hand-ed here I come, I've no-thing left— to give— you.

Take my heart and all I— am; who else,— Lord, can I run— to?

Ev-'ry part of me you see,— I'm an o - pen book be-fore— you.

Je-sus, take me as I am, I can come no o-ther way.— Your arms—

CCLI# 7043791

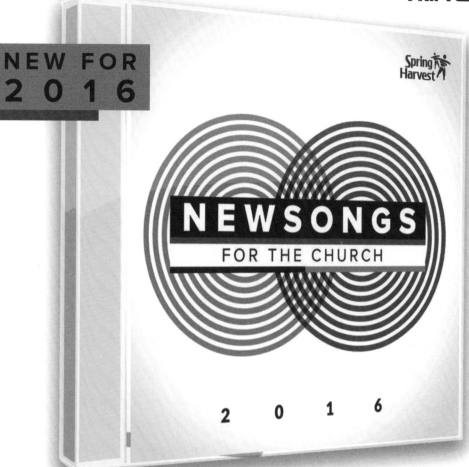

# EVERY PAINFUL DAY
# I'VE KNOWN
## [I BELEIVE]

Key = A

Sam Cox & Becki Cox

♩ = 72

**Verse**

1. Ev - 'ry pain - ful day I've known, and
You've been work - ing for my good, your
2. Help me now to lift my head through
I have known your faith - ful - ness, and

ev - 'ry door un - o - pened.
sov - 'reign hand will lead me.
pray'rs that seem un - an - swered;
you have ne - ver failed me.

**Pre-Chorus**

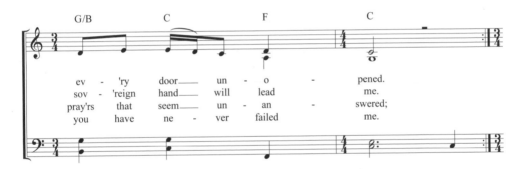

E-ven through the dark-est night, I know you won't for-sake me. And
E-ven in the val - ley low your good-ness ne - ver fails me.

**Chorus**

I be-lieve that you are God when all a - round gives way. And

CCLI# 7048168

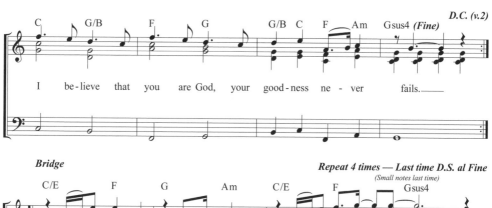

I be-lieve that you are God, your good-ness ne - ver fails.

**Bridge**

*Repeat 4 times — Last time D.S. al Fine*
(Small notes last time)

I__ will trust you and sur - ren - der, you__ are al - ways__ good.__
You__ are per - fect, al - ways faith - ful, you__ are al - ways__ good.__

# 6

# FOR WE TRUST IN OUR GOD
## [WE WILL NOT BE SHAKEN]

Key = D

Brian Johnson, Ben Fielding,
Bob Hartley, Bobby Strand & Chris Greely

♩ = 74

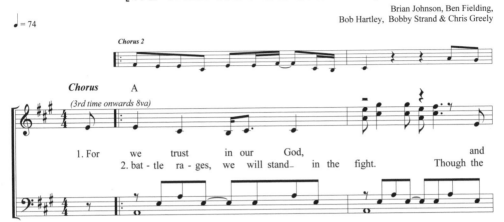

1. For we trust in our God, and
2. bat - tle ra - ges, we will stand in the fight. Though the

through his un - fail - ing love we will not be sha -
ar - mies rise up against us on all sides

*5th, 7th time to Coda (al Fine)*

- ken, we will not be sha - ken, we will not be sha - ken.

26

CCLI# 7029075

28

# 7

# FROM HIM, THROUGH HIM, AND TO HIM ARE ALL THINGS
## [GREATER]

Key = B♭

Ben Fielding, Chris Tomlin,
Ed Cash & Matt Redman

Capo 3 (G)

♩ = 74

*Verse*

1. From him, through him, and to him are all things; to God be the glo-ry.
   was, and is, and for-ev-er-will be;- to God be the glo-ry.

His Word en-dures from be-gin-ning to end; to God be the glo-ry,
His pow'r in us, his— strength for the weak; to God be the glo-ry

*Chorus*

to God be the glo-ry.
to God be the glo-ry.

Great-er is the One who lives in-

me! Great-er is the love of Je-sus! Great-er than my sin,

**CCLI# 7030449**

# 8

# FROM THE BREAKING OF
# THE DAYLIGHT
## [PLANS]

Key = C

Tim Hughes
& Nick Herbert

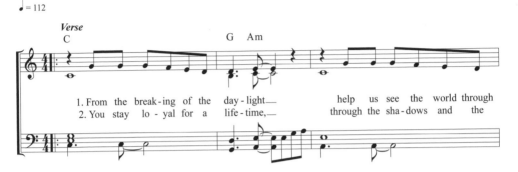

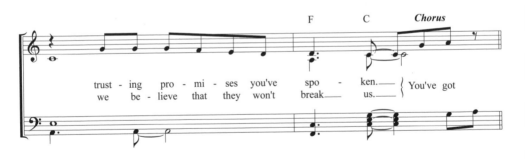

CCLI# 7043790

we are not a-lone.    Plans to— lead us home— in-to your heart,

*1° D.C.(v.2)*
*Last time D.S. al Fine*

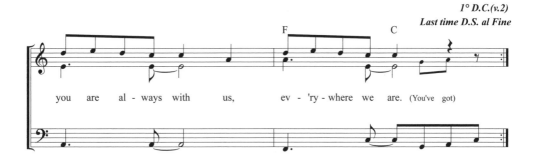

you    are    al - ways with    us,    ev - 'ry - where we    are. (You've got)

**Mid section**

On    and on,— your love— will ne - ver    stop        shin - ing down up - on    us,
On    and on— your love— will see us through,        e - ven    in    the sha - dows

ne - ver    let - ting up.                                                        (You've got)
we will trust in    you.

33

# 9

# GO IN PEACE

Key = D

Graham Kendrick
& Mark Tedder

♩ = 114

*Verse*

1. Go in peace
Christ, { to love and serve the Lord. Go in peace, go in peace. 1. Go in 2. In the name of And he goes be-fore us, walks be-side; will ne-ver leave or for-sake us. And he us. 1. Go in

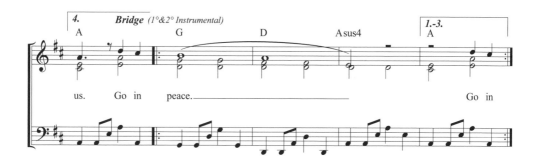

Bridge *(1°&2° Instrumental)*

us. Go in peace._____ Go in

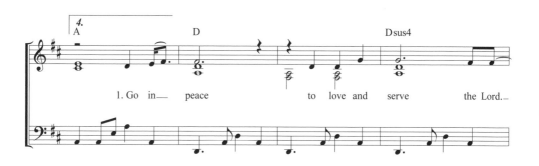

1. Go in___ peace       to love and serve       the Lord.___

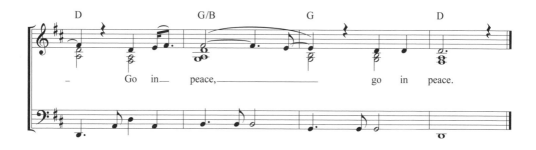

Go in___ peace,_____ go in peace.

# 10

# GOD, YOU CAN TELL THE WAVES 'BE STILL'
## [SONGS IN THE NIGHT]

Key = A♭

Matt Redman,
Jonas Myrin & Jason Ingram

Capo 1 (G)

♩ = 80

Verse

1. God, you can—

tell the waves 'be still',—— tell the o - cean roar to— pass,—
part the rag - ing sea,—— bring the mi - ra - cle I need,—
I am in the storm,—— Lord, the storm is not in— me,—

Lord, un - til it—— does, I'll wait— here.
Lord, un - til it—— comes, I'll wait— here.
you will be my—— peace, I'll wait— here.

Last time to Coda 2

1.
2. God, you can—

2.,3.
(I'll wait here.)

Chorus
And I will

CCLI# 7043174

38

# GRANDER EARTH HAS QUAKED BEFORE
## [IT IS WELL]

Key = G

Kristene DiMarco

CCLI# 7021972

# 12 HEAR OUR CRY, OH KING OF HEAVEN
## [HOPE AND GLORY]

Key = D

Tim Hughes,
Martin Smith & Nick Herbert

CCLI# 7043793

_land; Christ a - lone, our hope and glo - ry,— Christ a - lone in you— we

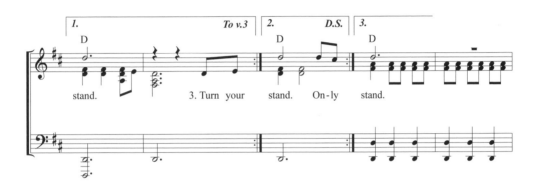

stand. 3. Turn your stand. On-ly stand.

We be - lieve——— our God is— migh - ty, we be-

lieve——— our God is— here, we be - lieve——— our King is com - ing, Christ a-

# 13

# HOW SWEET THE SOUND
# OF JESUS' NAME
## [HOW SWEET THE SOUND]

Key = G

Alistair Metcalfe
& Matt Britton

1. How sweet the

| | | | | | | |
|---|---|---|---|---|---|---|
| sound | of Je - sus' | name | to | those who've | found | their hope in |
| sound | of Je - sus' | name: | my | cross his | cross, | my pain his |
| sound | of Je - sus' | name, | a | song to | si - lence all | my |
| sound, | a hymn of | praise | that | ech - oes | down | through end - less |

| | | | | | |
|---|---|---|---|---|---|
| Him; | the name of | love, | of life, of | breath, | of pow'r so |
| pain. | His love, like | nails | thrust hard through | bone, | was splin - tered |
| shame; | as love dis - | played | through nail - pierced | hands, | for - gives the |
| days | and stirs the | heart | of ev - 'ry | one | whose li - ber - |

| | | | | | |
|---|---|---|---|---|---|
| strong, | it con - quered | death. | The name my | tongue | will al - ways |
| for | my heart of | stone. | My debt was | paid, | my soul set |
| wretch | and bids me | stand. | All doubt, all | fear, | left in the |
| ty | his mer - cy | won | One day I'll | stand | be - fore his |

45

CCLI# 7053427

Oh what, oh what a name.

Je - sus, we love your name.

THIS SONG IS FEATURED ON **NEWSONGS FOR THE CHURCH 2016**

# 14

# HUMBLY I STAND,
# AN OFFERING
## [EVERYTHING AND NOTHING LESS]

Key = A

Aaron Ivey,
Chris McClarney & Jason Ingram

CCLI# 7040553

less,    my best,—    my—all.—

You de-serve my ev-'ry    breath,    my life,—

—    my song.—

**Chorus**

I  sur-ren-der,—  I  sur-ren-der— all——    oh,—  I  sur-ren-der,

*1.*                    *D.C.(v.2)*   *2.,4.,6.,7.*        *D.S. (al fine)*

I  sur-ren-der—all.—

50

BE COMPLETELY HUMBLE AND GENTLE;

BE PATIENT,

BEARING WITH ONE ANOTHER IN LOVE

**EPHESIANS 4:2**

## 15

# I CAN SEE THE
# PROMISED LAND
## [EVERY GIANT WILL FALL]

Key = B♭

Capo 3 (G)

Rend Collective

♩ = 112

**Intro** Em7 / C2 / G
Gm7 / E♭2 / B♭

Em7 / C2 / G   **Verse** Em7 / C2
Gm7 / E♭2 / B♭         Gm7 / E♭2

1. I can see the pro-mised land.—
   fears like Je-ri-cho,—
   hope with-in the fight,—

G   Em7 / C2   G
B♭  Gm7 / E♭2  B♭

though there's pain with-in the plan,——— There is
build their walls a-round my soul.——— When my
in the wars that rage in-side.——— Though the

Em7 / C2 / G   **1.** C2   Em7
Gm7 / E♭2 / B♭      E♭2   Gm7

vic-t'ry in the end.——— Your love is— my bat-tle— cry!
heart is o-ver-thrown,——— your
sha-dows steal the light,——— your

CCLI# 7047084

-'ry chain,___ for-e___ver reign,___ King Je-sus!___ No great___-er name,___ no high-

-er name,___ no strong___-er name___ than___ Je-sus.___ You o___-ver-came,___ broke ev-

-'ry___ chain,___ for-e___ver reign,___ King___ Je-sus!_____ Ev-'ry

**⊕ Coda**

pos___-si-ble with you. Whoah,_____ Oh,

no___-thing is im-pos___-si-ble.

# 16

# I CAST MY MIND
# TO CALVARY
## [OH PRAISE THE NAME (ANASTASIS)]

Key = C

Benjamin Hastings,
Dean Ussher & Marty Sampson

♩ = 72

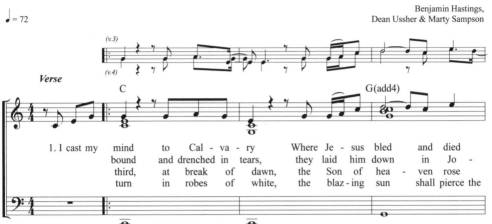

**Verse**

1. I cast my mind to Cal - va - ry Where Je - sus bled and died
   bound and drenched in tears, they laid him down in Jo -
   third, at break of dawn, the Son of hea - ven rose
   turn in robes of white, the blaz - ing sun shall pierce the

for me. I see his wounds, his hands, his feet; My Sa - viour
seph's tomb. The en - trance sealed by hea - vy stone: Mes - si - ah
a - gain. O tram - pled death, where is your sting? The an - gels
night. And I will rise a - mong the saints, my gaze trans -

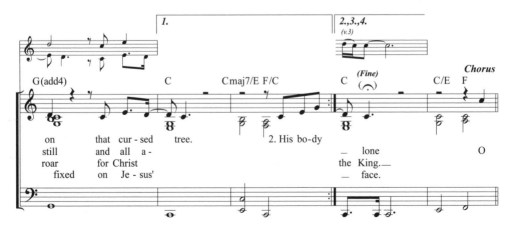

on that cur - sed tree. 2. His bo - dy
still and all a - lone
roar for Christ the King.—
fixed on Je - sus' face.

CCLI# 7037787

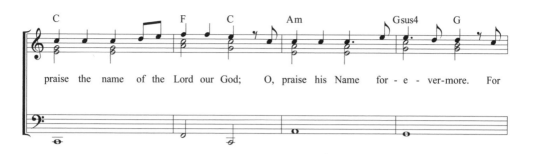

praise the name of the Lord our God; O, praise his Name for - e - ver-more. For

*Last time to Coda* ⊕

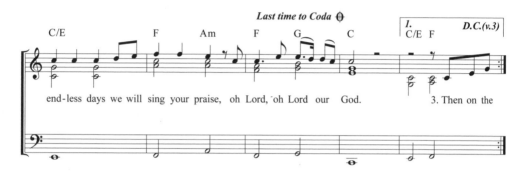

end-less days we will sing your praise, oh Lord, oh Lord our God.

3. Then on the

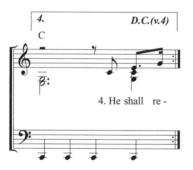

4. He shall re -

# I HAVE A HOME
## [ABIDE WITH ME]

Key = B

Matt Maher, Matt Redman,
Jason Ingram & David Crowder

Capo 4 (G)

CCLI# 7038447

# I LOOK UPON THE FACE
## [WIDE OPEN SPACES]

Key = C

Rachel Mathias, Cath Woolridge
& Matt Richley

♩ = 56

1. I look up - on the face of him who took my shame;
2. Through tri - als and through pain our hope in Christ re - mains;
3. Through love I'm re - con - ciled, in Christ I'm jus - ti - fied;
4. His love is me - lo - dy, heav'n's song sung o - ver me,

I'm shel - tered from dis - grace by Je - sus.
by faith through grace we come to Je - sus.
in free - dom I will live for Je - sus.
heart burst - ing full and free in Je - sus. } Stand-ing in

wide o - pen spa - ces of your grace, lift-ing up your name and shout-ing out your

CCLI# 7035049

# 19

# I WAS NOWHERE
## [THE WAY]

Key = B

Capo 4 (G)

♩ = 76

Ben Cantelon,
Nick Herbert & Tim Hughes

*Verse*

G#m(Em)　E(C)　B(G)　G#m(Em)　E(C)

1. I__ was no-where, you came to my res-cue,　from the grave I've been
2. All my days are se-cure in your pro-mise,　ne-ver stand-ing a-

B(G)　G#m(Em)　E(C)　B(G)

raised.　When I need-ed a sa-viour to save__ me,
lone.　You're the truth, you're the life, you're my fu-ture,

G#m(Em)　E(C)　B(G)　G#m(Em)　E(C)

Je-sus, you made a__ way.__　I__ was blind, but these
Je-sus, you made a__ way.__　I'm__ a-live in that

B(G)　G#m(Em)　E(C)　B(G)

eyes have been o-pened,　now I walk in__ the light.
love that__ you give__ me,　free to dance once a-gain.

CCLI# 7023304

Ev - 'ry step on this road I__ will fol - low, Je - sus, you made a__ way.
You will lead me from glo - ry to glo - ry, Je - sus, you made a__ way.

*Chorus*

You are the way.__ You are the way.__

*5th time to Coda 1*

1. Lost and dead, but your love came to find me,
2. You're the light shin - ing bright in__ the dark - ness, } Je - sus you are the way.

*1.,3.*

*2.,4.*

You are the __ Je - sus, the on - ly__ way.__

*repeat 4 times*

*1.*

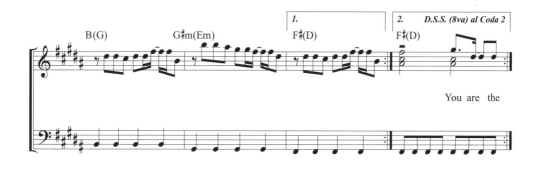

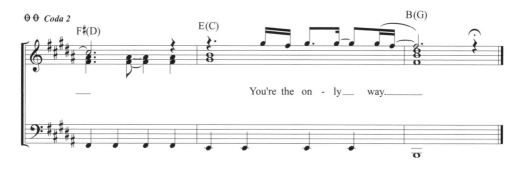

# SPRING HARVEST
## song search

If you need help to find a song on a particular theme or Scripture passage, or just want to know which of the Spring Harvest songbooks or albums features the song you're after - use our song search.

» search online at **www.springharvest.org/songsearch**

# I WILL WAIT ON YOU LORD
## [FOREVER YOURS]

Key = B♭

Capo 3 (G)

Martin Smith,
Matt Bray & Henry Milne

♩ = 135

1. I will wait on you Lord. I
   I will walk with you Lord. Yes I

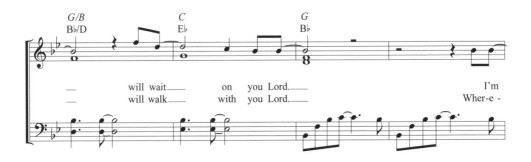

will wait on you Lord. I'm
will walk with you Lord. Wher-e-

not go-ing a-ny-where so I
-ver you go I'll al-ways fol-low. So I

will wait on you Lord. I'm
will walk with you, Lord.

CCLI# 7043163

al - ways be mine.___ I'm for - e - ver yours.___

I'm for - e - ver yours._____

2. I___ ___

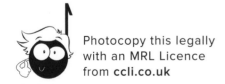

Photocopy this legally
with an MRL Licence
from ccli.co.uk

# I'LL BE THE ALTAR
## [LET ME BURN]

Key = E

Andy Smith

72

# IMMORTAL, INVISIBLE

Key = G

Tom McConnell

1. Im - mor - tal, in - vi - si - ble, God on - ly wise; in light in - ac - ces - si - ble, hid from our eyes. Most Ho - ly, most glo - rious, the An - cient of

2. Though wea - ry and help - less and dead in our sin, Lord Je - sus you came to re - deem us a - gain. Your blood is our right - eous - ness, for we have

3. No long - er con - demned or as sin - ner's re - viled, great Sa - viour, your blood means we are re - con - ciled. to the Fa - ther who'll see us as spot - less and

*Last time to Coda* ⊕

Verse

CCLI# 7054304

4. O Spi - rit of Christ come a - live in - side

me and show the great po - wer that has set me

free. Once or - phans, we now are called daugh - ters and sons and

co - heirs with Christ whom sal - va - tion has won. Now we know

*Coda*

# 23

# I'VE COME HERE TODAY TO WORSHIP AGAIN
## [ALIVE WITH WORSHIP]

Key = G

Simon Brading
& Jotham Oakley

♩ = 104

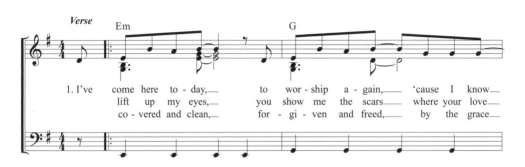

**Verse**

1. I've come here to-day,___ to wor-ship a-gain,___ 'cause I know___
lift up my eyes,___ you show me the scars___ where your love___
co-vered and clean,___ for-gi-ven and freed, by the grace___

___ that my Fa-ther's here.___ My Fa-ther has shown me a way,___ a-
___ paid ev-'ry-thing. Paid for___ me to live with my God,___ no
___ that you stand___ me in. I'm stand-ing, my feet on a rock,___ my

way from the pain___ of the sin___ that I've stum-bled in.___ 2. You
long-er a-part, for you bled,___ and you died___ for me.___
fu-ture in God, and my soul,___ you've count-ed free.___

**Chorus**

My soul___ is a-live___ with wor-ship, I'm
soul___ is a-live___ with won-der, I'm

CCLI# 7048165

sing - ing a-gain 'cause my heart____ it o - ver - flows____ with the love____ and mer - cy of
wel-comed a-gain_ be - fore you____ my Fa - ther, Oh,____ how I love____ to wor - ship

you, my____ God. My ___ God. Yeah!____
you, my____

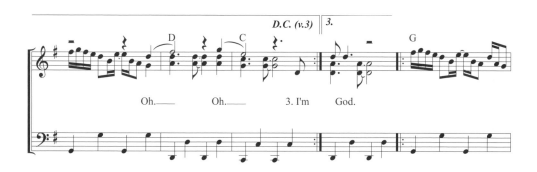

Oh.____ Oh.____ 3. I'm God.

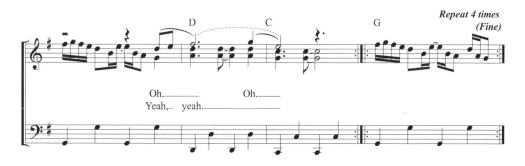

Oh.____ Oh.____
Yeah, yeah.____

# I'VE HEARD A THOUSAND STORIES OF WHAT THEY THINK YOU'RE LIKE
## [GOOD, GOOD FATHER]

Key = A

Pat Barrett & Tony Brown

CCLI# 7036612

82

*D.S.(with repeat) al Coda*

*Coda*

# JESUS CHRIST, EMMANUEL
## [ALL OUR HALLELUJAHS]

Key = F

Capo 3 (D)

♩ = 77

Matt Richley & Cath Woolridge

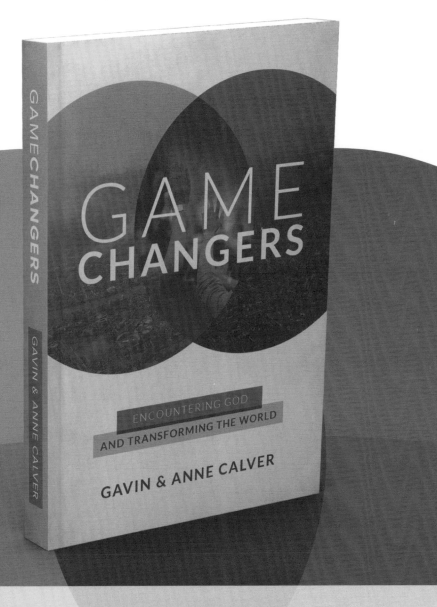

The Game Changers theme guide, taking you through encounters in the life of Moses, and on to being a Game Changer in your own sphere

# 26

# JESUS, JESUS, HOW I TRUST YOU
## [EYES ON YOU]

Key = G

Kristene DiMarco,
Josh Silverberg & Matt Armstrong

1. Je-sus, Je-sus, how___ I trust___ you, How I've proved___ you more___
2. Je-sus, Je-sus, how___ I trust___ you, I'll take you at___ your ve-

___ and more.___ My life's most pre-cious trea-sures stored,___ safe
-ry word.___ Through un-knowns and my ques-tions, Lord,___ there's

in your___ e-ter-nal arms.___ Eyes on you, Lord, eyes___ on_
grace e-nough for them all.___

___you, through the laugh-ter, through the___ pain. My on-ly an-swer, my on-ly___

*(D.S. (final chorus repeat) al Fine)*

G        C    D    G
*(Fine)*

_____truth:    eyes on    you, Lord,    eyes_ on    you.    (Eyes on)

**Bridge**

C           G

Je-sus,   Je    -    sus.    Je-sus,   Je    -    sus,

C           G

how I   trust you,    how I   trust you.    Je-sus,   Je    -    sus.

C           G

Je-sus,   Je    -    sus.    Je-sus,   Je    -    sus,

Em           G        *D.S.*

how I   trust you,    how I   trust you.    Je-sus,   Je    -    sus.    Eyes on

# 27

# LET FAITH ARISE IN SPITE OF WHAT I SEE
## [GOD OF MIRACLES]

Key = B♭

Capo 3 (G)

Chad Bohi,
Chris McClarney & Jordan Frye

♩ = 75

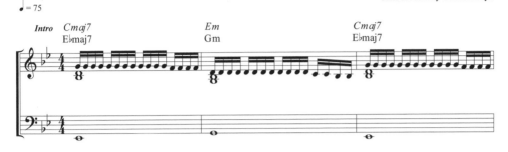

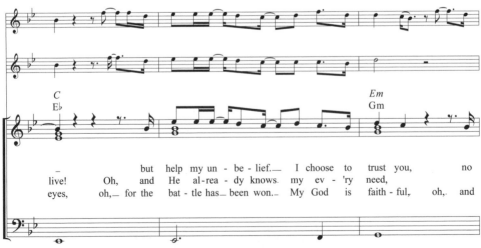

1. Let faith a-rise in spite of what I see; Lord I be-lieve
For my Cham-pi-on's not dead, He is a-
3. Let faith a-rise and see the king-dom come, I lift my

but help my un-be-lief. I choose to trust you, no
live! Oh, and He al-rea-dy knows. my ev-'ry need,
eyes, oh, for the bat-tle has been won. My God is faith-ful, oh, and

CCLI# 7040599

**1.**
*C*
*Eb*

mat - ter what__ I feel,__ let faith a - rise. 2. Let faith a-
sure - ly He__ will come and re - scue
ev - 'ry sin - gle word__ he said is

**2.,3.**

*Cmaj7*
*Ebmaj7*

𝄉 *Chorus*
*Em* *C* *G* *D*
*Gm* *Eb* *Bb* *F*

me.
__ true, oh.__

God of mi - ra - cles,__ come,__ we need your

*Em* *C* *G* *D* *Em* *C*
*Gm* *Eb* *Bb* *F* *Gm* *Eb*

su - per - na - tu - ral__ love__ to break through. No-thing's im - pos - si - ble:__

*1° D.C.(v.3)*
*3° 4° D.S. (al Coda)*
*Last time to Coda* ⊕

*G* *D* *Em* *C*
*Bb* *F* *Gm* *Eb* *G* *D*
*Bb* *F*

You're the God of mi - ra - cles.__

JESUS LOOKED AT THEM AND SAID,

"WITH MAN THIS IS IMPOSSIBLE,

BUT WITH GOD ALL THINGS ARE POSSIBLE"

**MATTHEW 19:26**

# 28

# LET THE KING OF MY HEART
## [KING OF MY HEART]

Key = A

John Mark McMillan
& Sarah McMillan

1. Let the King of my heart be the moun - tain where I run, the
King of my heart be the wind____ in - side my sails, the

foun - tain I drink from, oh, he is my____ song. Let the King of my heart be the sha-
an - chor in the waves, oh, he is my____ song. Let the King of my heart be the fire

(Small notes 2°)

Chorus

- dow where I hide, the ran - som for my life, oh, he is my____ song.
___ in - side my veins, the e - cho of my days, oh, he is my____ song.
You are

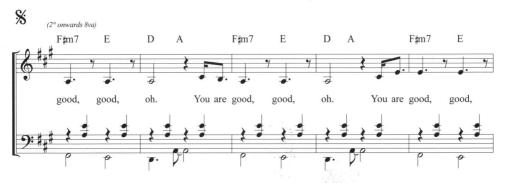

(2° onwards 8va)

good, good, oh. You are good, good, oh. You are good, good,

CCLI# 7046145

# 29

# MIGHTY IN BATTLE, PERFECT IN LOVE
## [UNTO YOUR NAME]

Key = G

Barrett & Ben Smith

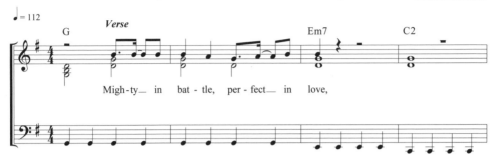

Migh-ty— in bat-tle, per-fect— in love,

awe-some— in won-der, faith-ful and—— just.

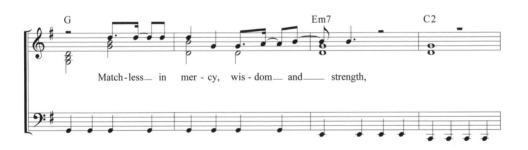

Match-less— in mer-cy, wis-dom— and—— strength,

you can— be trust-ed— in all of— your—— ways. We'll sing it out.

CCLI# 7036674

Your _____ name _____ is wor - thy _____ of

praise. _____

# MY SOUL LONGS FOR JESUS

Key = A-B-D♭

Ed Cash

CCLI# 7042545

longs for Je - sus, longs for Je - sus. My soul longs for

Je - sus a - lone

*Verse*

5. My

soul longs for Je - sus, what a glo - ri - ous day, when the trou - bles of the

a - ges shall swift-ly pass a - way. With the ar-mies of hea-ven he will car - ry us

home; How I long for you, Je - sus, O come, Je - sus, come.

# 31

# NO EYE HAS SEEN
## [FASCINATE]

Key = F

Capo 3 (D)

Lou Fellingham & Nathan Fellingham

♩ = 80

**Verse**

1. No eye has seen, no ear has heard the full ex-tent of your great worth. The Lord of all, the cen-tre-piece, un-matched in love and ma-je-sty.

2. You fa-shioned all with skill-ful hands, the great-est care in ev-'ry strand. From fur-thest stars to deep-est seas, your love is there a-bun-dant-ly.

3. the earth is filled with your sup-ply, you say the word, you sa-tis-fy. We rise and fade at your com-mand, you are the cry of ev-'ry man.

**Chorus**

You fa-sci-nate me, you are a-stound-ing, you're ne-ver end-ing, you're beau-ti-ful.

CCLI# 7028210

Your ways are high - er, your think - ing deep - er, your wis - dom great - er,

*1.*

*D.C. (v.2)* *2.* *D.S.*

you're beau - ti - ful. you're beau - ti - ful.

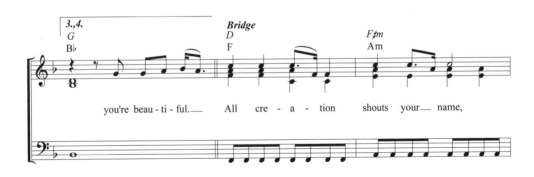

*3.,4.* **Bridge**

you're beau - ti - ful.___ All cre - a - tion shouts your___ name,

sings your glo - ry, tells your___ fame. Some things hid - den,

some things—seen,——— you're such a sweet my - ste - ry.———

*Coda:*

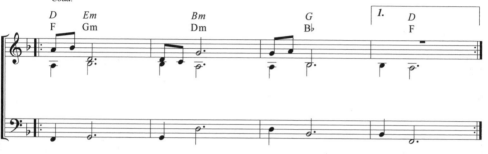

# LIVE WORSHIP FROM
# SPRING HARVEST

## PRE-ORDER NOW

FEATURING LEAD WORSHIPPERS:
CATHY BURTON    BEN CANTELON    LOU FELLINGHAM
NICK HERBERT    CHRIS McCLARNEY    SOUND OF WALES

# 32

# O LOVE THAT WILL NOT LET ME GO

Key = D/E

Lyrics: George Mattheson & Ralph Manuel
Music: Rachel Mathias
Chorus: Cath Woolridge

♩ = 72

love that will not let me—— go, I rest my wea-ry soul in thee.
joy that seek-est me through—— pain, I can - not close my heart to thee.

I give thee—— back the life I—— owe, that in thine
I trace the—— rain - bow through the—— rain, and feel the

o - cean depths its flow,— that in thine o - cean depths its flow,— that in thine
pro - mise is— not vain, and feel the pro - mise is— not vain,— and feel the

# 33

# OUR GOD IS A KEEPER OF HIS WORD
## [POUR OUT]

Key = A

Amber Hillen
& Abby Brotherston

♩ = 76

1. Our___ God___

is a keep-er of___ his word,___ he is all___ he
is the an-swer for___ our land,___ he is all___ we

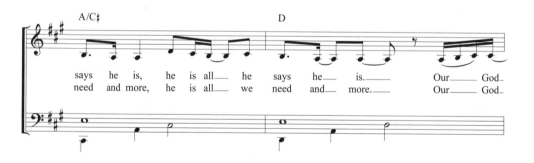

says he is, he is all___ he says he___ is.___ Our___ God___
need and more, he is all___ we need and___ more.___ Our___ God___

has said it in___ his word,___ he will pour___ his
wants to pour on us,___ he's search-ing for___ an

112

# 34

# OUR SCARS ARE A SIGN
## [IT IS WELL WITH MY SOUL]

Key = E

Capo 4 (C)

♩ = 80

Words by Horatio G. Spafford
Music by Philip P. Bliss
Arr: Matt Redman & Beth Redman

1. Our scars are a sign of grace in our lives, and Fa-ther, how you brought us through. When deep were the wounds, and dark was the night, the pro-mise of your love, you proved.

2. Weep-ing may come, re-main for a night, but joy will paint the morn-ing sky. You're there in the fast, you're there in the feast, your faith-ful-ness will al-ways shine.

114

lead us through bat - tles,) you lead us to bles - sing, (you lead us to bles - sing,) and

you make us fruit - ful, (you make us fruit - ful,) in the land of our suf - f'ring, God.

And it is well, it is well with my soul.

It is

**Coda**

It is well, it is well with my soul.

# 35

# OVERHEAD, SKIES ARE DARK
## [I WILL HOPE]

Key = C

David Lyon

♩ = 156

1. O-ver - head,_____ skies are dark, but I
_____ and the flame is a
_____ torn in two, but I
_____ and the fight is a

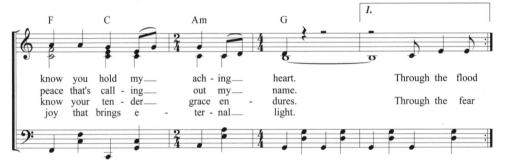

know you hold my___ ach - ing___ heart. Through the flood
peace that's call - ing out my___ name.
know your ten - der grace en - dures. Through the fear
joy that brings e - ter - nal light.

I will hope in___ you,___ my Sa - viour. And I will

hope in___ you,___ De - fen - der. And I will hope in___ you___ when

king - doms col-lide:___ You are___ my___ life.

*1.,2.,4.* *(Ad lib violin)*

*(Fine)* *1.* *D.C. (v.2)* *3.* *D.S.S. al fine*

2. O-ver-whelmed,___

*2.* **Bridge**

New ev - 'ry morn - ing, your mer - cies___ O God;

love e - ver - last-ing, your un-chang - ing word. word.

# 36 OVERWHELMED BUT I WON'T BREAK
## [IN GOD WE TRUST]

Key = D

Ben Fielding,
Eric Liljero & Reuben Morgan

CCLI# 7037224

-ways be__ e - nough.__ } Now in God we trust, in his name we hope, I know__
-mise ne - ver fails.__ }

__ God will not be sha - ken. God is here with us, he's al - rea - dy won, I know__

*Last time to Coda*

__ God will not be sha - ken.

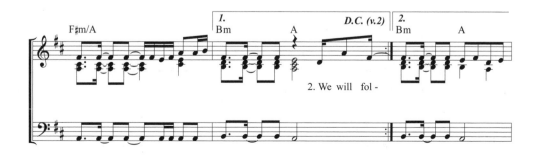

2. We will fol -

# PRAISE UNBROKEN
## [UNBROKEN PRAISE]

Key = G

Matt Redman & Jonas Myrin

♩ = 66

CCLI# 7043173

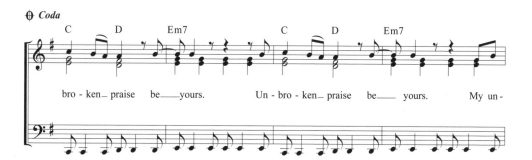

# SPIRIT OF GOD

Key = C#m

Capo 4 (Am)

Geraldine Latty & Carey Luce

♩ = 70

**Sequence:**
Intro *x2*
A *x2*
B *x2*
C *x2*
A *x2*
A + B *x2*
A+B+C *x2*
Chorus *x 3*
Ending

CCLI# 7026285

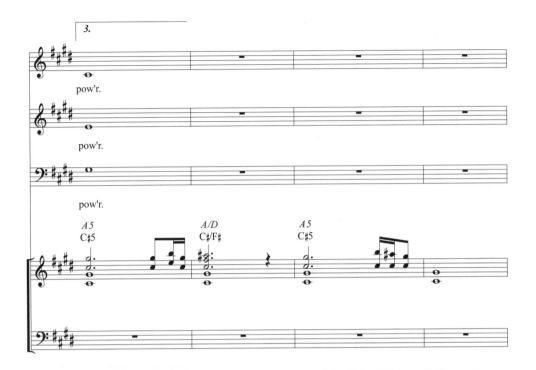

3.

pow'r.

pow'r.

pow'r.

**Ending**

Spir-it of God, bring free-dom to ev-'ry heart.

BUT THE ADVOCATE, THE HOLY SPIRIT,

WHOM THE FATHER WILL SEND IN MY NAME,

WILL TEACH YOU ALL THINGS

AND WILL REMIND YOU OF EVERYTHING I HAVE SAID TO YOU

JOHN 14:26

# 39

# STANDING IN THIS PLACE OF TEARS
## [LEAD ME TO THE ROCK]

Key = E

David Lyon & Lindsay Potter

1. Stand-ing in this place of tears,—— with hurt that on-ly you can heal——
2. Run-ning to a brigh-ter day,—— with hope that makes the wound-ed whole..

trust-ing that I will be free,—— hear my—— cry,—
Trust-ing I can find your peace,—— hear my—— cry,—

hear my—— cry——
hear my—— cry.——

Lead me to the rock that is high-er than I,——

lead me to the One who can-not be sha - ken. Lead me to the rock that is

high-er than I,— lead me to the Sav-ing— One.—

Age to age you stay the same,

through the pain and suf-fer-ing. Age to age you will re-main,

God our Fa - ther, strong— for - e - ver.—

# 40

# THE LORD IS OUR SALVATION
## [NOT BE MOVED]

Key = G

Jon Egan, Glenn Packiam,
Dustin Smith & Fanny Crosby

1. The Lord is our sal-va-tion, ho-ly, great and just, our

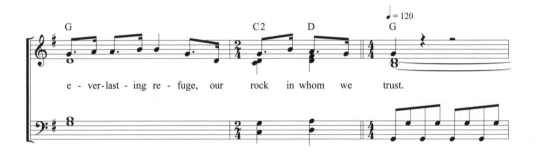

e-ver-last-ing re-fuge, our rock in whom we trust.

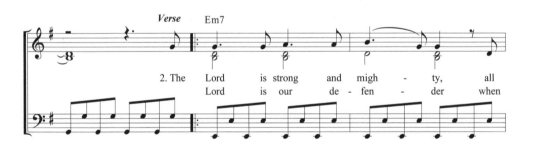

2. The Lord is strong and migh-ty, all
Lord is our de-fen-der when

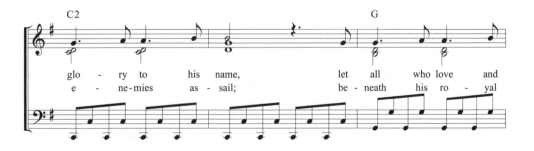

glo-ry to his name, let all who love and
e-ne-mies as-sail; be-neath his ro-yal

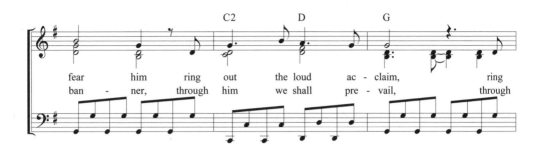

fear him ring out the loud ac - claim, ring
ban - ner, through him we shall pre - vail, through

*(Small notes v.2)*

*Chorus* 𝄉 *(D.S. 1st time 8vb)*

out the loud ac - claim.
him we shall pre - vail.

*(1st time omit small notes)*

Oh,— God you are— our—

rock, our rock, we will not be— moved;— God you are— our—

*(D.S. at pitch)*

hope, our hope, we will not— be, we will not be moved,—

132

# 41

# THIS IS A HOLY MOMENT
## [HOLY MOMENT]

Key = C

Chris McClarney
& Jason Ingram

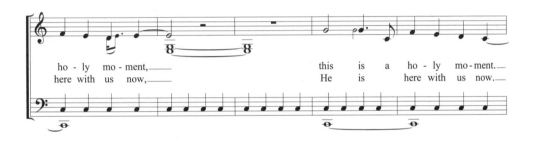

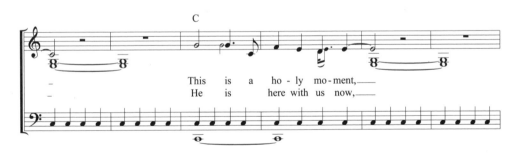

CCLI# 7040563

134

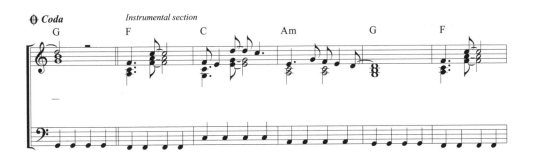

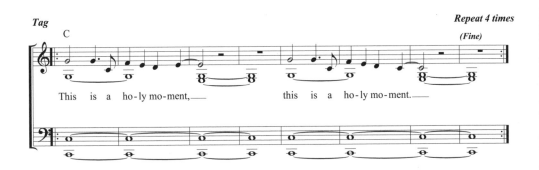

This is a ho-ly mo-ment,___ this is a ho-ly mo-ment.___

Photocopy this legally
with an MRL Licence
from **ccli.co.uk**

# 42

# WAKE UP MY SOUL AND TURN TO HIM
## [HALLELUJAH]

Key = C

Lou Fellingham,
Nathan Fellingham & Sam Cox

♩ = 140

1. Wake up my
2. Our God is

soul and turn—— to him,——       come to the gi - ver of    good - ness,——
here with po - wer to save,——      no one too far—— from the    reach    of——

joy    and—— peace.                                        One heart, one
his    great—— grace.                                      His migh - ty

voice  lift   up—— to him;——     re - mem-ber the won - ders of   mer - cy——
love  lights  up—— the way,——    rea - dy to of - fer for - give - ness—— in

# 43

# WATCHING, WAITING FOR YOUR FIRE AGAIN
## [WILDFIRE]

Key = C

Sam Bailey, Nick Herbert,
Ben Cantelon & Tim Hughes

♩. = 63

**℅ Verse**

*(Small notes vv.2,3)*

1. Watch-ing, wait-ing for your fire a-gain;
2. Just one look, one touch would be e-nough;
3. As Your Spi-rit moved up on the wa-ters,

may we know your pre-sence in this place.
breathe your ho-ly breath, your fire of love.
ev-'ry heart a-waits new life a-gain.

**Chorus 1**

*(1° to v.2)*

C ... Em/B

Spi - rit,___ Spi - rit move up - on___ this___

Am7 ... F2 ... C

ground, in this mo - ment would you come.___

Em/B ... C ... Em/B

Wild - fire, speed___ your love,

F2 ... C/G ... *1.* Am7 ... Em/B ... C ... Dm7

burn in us___ a - gain,___ wild - fire.___

Like wild - fire, God___ a - bove,

how we need_____ you_____ now_____ how we_need_____ you_____

now_____ how we_need_____ you_____ now_____ Wild -

fire._____

# 44

# WE ALL STAND AMAZED
## [POWER IN THE CROSS]

Key = F♯

Capo 4 (D)

Derek Johnson,
Anthony Skinner & Gabe Kossol

♩ = 66

*Verse* D / F♯ ... G / B

1. We all___ stand a-mazed, in awe of a-maz-ing grace,
2. Now we are___ made a-live, in free-dom like a fire

Em / G♯m ... G / B ... D / F♯

the di-vide has___ been e-rased, we thank___ you. All sin is washed a-way,
burn-ing with one de-sire, we thank___ you. We will spend all our lives,

G / B ... Em / G♯m

you a-lone___ have saved___ the___ day, we are for-e-ver changed, we
filled with the___ hope of Christ who paid the fi-nal price, we

CCLI# 7032510

thank___ you.
thank___ you.

Let ev - 'ry heart, ev - 'ry tongue___

come sing___ of your re - demp - tion.___ There's po - wer in the

cross, where you proved your love, the on - ly sa - cri - fice,___ strong e - nough to

save___ us. You rose in vic - to - ry, to let the whole world see love has made a

way, hope is ne - ver lost, there's po - wer in the cross.

# WE ARE WAITING

Key = D

Leslie Jordan, Alli Rogers,
David Leonard & Fanny Crosby

CCLI# 7049336

# WHAT A SAVIOUR

Key = B

Capo 4 (G)

Chris Davenport & Joel Houston

CCLI# 7047248

Sa - viour, I will praise you al - ways.___ Oh,___ oh,___

oh,___ oh.___ 2. Hea-ven's praise you al - ways.___ And oh, what

praise you al - ways. Oh, what praise you al - ways.___ I will

praise you al - ways,___ yeah.___

152

cross where Je - sus took my___ shame,                    Oh what

ev - 'ry breath will sing a - - - gain.

praise you al - ways.   Oh, I will praise you    al - ways.   Oh, I will

praise you al - ways.   I will praise_ you    al - ways.___

# WHAT FORTUNE LIES BEYOND THE STARS
## [TOUCH THE SKY]

Key = A

Joel Houston,
Dylan Thomas & Michael Guy Chislett

♩ = 90

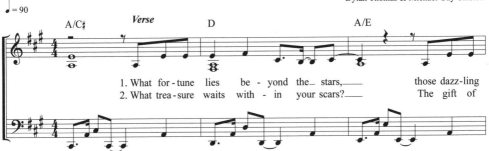

**Verse**

A/C♯   D   A/E

1. What for-tune lies be-yond the stars, those dazz-ling
2. What trea-sure waits with-in your scars? The gift of

F♯m   A/C♯   D

heights too vast to climb? I got so high to fall so far,
free-dom gold can't buy. I bought the world and sold my heart,

𝄋 **Chorus (8va on D.S.)**

A/E   F♯m   A/C♯

(v.2)

but I found hea-ven as love swept low. (ground) My heart beat-ing,
you tra-ded hea-ven to have me a-gain.

D   A/E   F♯m

my soul breath-ing; I found my life when I laid it down.

154

CCLI# 7033417

Up - ward__ fall-ing,____ spi - rit____ soar-ing;____ I touch__ the sky__

**3rd time D.S (Chorus repeat)**
**4th time jump to Bridge (8va)**

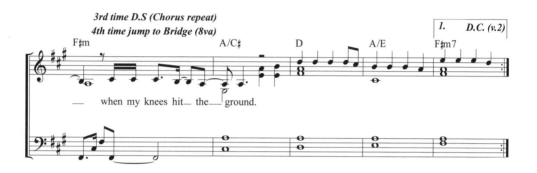

__ when my knees hit__ the__ ground.

*1.* D.C. (v.2)

*2.*

*Bridge*

(ground.) Find me here at your feet a-gain, ev-'ry-thing I am reach-ing

155

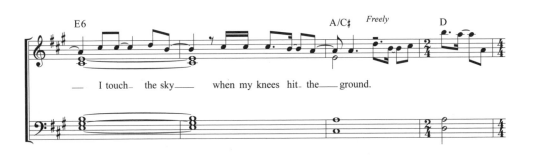

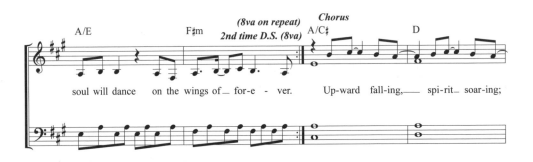

# WHEN DARKNESS DEEPENS
## [HERE WITH ME]

Key = C

Tim Hughes,
Nick Herbert & Phil Wickham

CCLI# 7043786

# WHEN I CALL
## [PSALM 4]

Key = D

Geraldine Latty
& Carey Luce

# IN PEACE I WILL LIE DOWN

## AND SLEEP, FOR YOU ALONE,

## LORD, MAKE ME DWELL IN SAFETY

**PSALM 4:8**

# WHEN I WAS LOST
## [ALLELUIA, HE HAS LOVED US]

Key = E♭

Capo 3 (C)

Tom McConnell

(Whoah,_____ whoah.)_____

1. When I was lost my guil - ty heart was lead - ing me a - stray;
2. O what a gift so free - ly gi - ven and grace so un - de - served,
3. The po - wer of our glo - ri - ous God the grave could not con - tain;

I put my trust in___ i - dols that shall fal - ter and de - cay.
that Je - sus came from heav'n to earth to serve and not be served.
Death is de - feat - ed___ once for all be - cause he rose a - gain.

Whilst in the depths of my de - spair, the sin - less Sa - viour
For all the wrong that I have done, my Lord has paid the
Je - sus,___ you and you a - lone sus - tain me and suf -

CCLI# 7054303

*(v.3)*

| Am7 | G | C | | F | C | | G |
| Cm7 | B♭ | E♭ | | A♭ | E♭ | | B♭ |

died, and bore the wrath for all my sin— when he was cru-ci-
price, and re-con-ciled me to his throne by Je-sus' sa-cri-
fice. Al - le - lu - ia! I'm for - gi-ven and— made a - live with

**Tag 1**

| | Am | | G | C | | F |
| | Cm | | B♭ | E♭ | | A♭ |
| C | | | | | | |
| E♭ | | | | | | |

fied. (Whoah,————————————— whoah.)————
fice.
Christ.

| 1.,3.,5. | | 2.,4.,6. | | **Tag 2** | | |
| C | G/B | C | D.C. (v.2,3.) | F | Am | G |
| E♭ | B♭/D | E♭ | | A♭ | Cm | B♭ |

— Al - le - lu - ia! He has loved us so a - bun - dant -

**Repeat 4 times**

| C | F | Am | G | C ( ⌒ ) |
| E♭ | A♭ | Cm | B♭ | E♭ |

ly; brought from death to life be-cause my God has ran-somed me.

163

# WHEN MY FEARS ARE OVERTAKING
## [YOU ARE MY PEACE]

Key = A♭

Capo 1 (G)

Lou Fellingham, Nathan Fellingham,
Sam Cox & Nick Herbert

♩ = 76

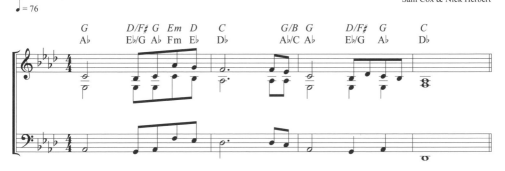

**Verse**

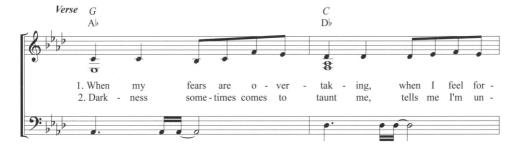

1. When my fears are o-ver-tak-ing, when I feel for-
2. Dark - ness some-times comes to taunt me, tells me I'm un-

sa - ken, God is by my side. But
wor - thy of the Fa-ther's love.

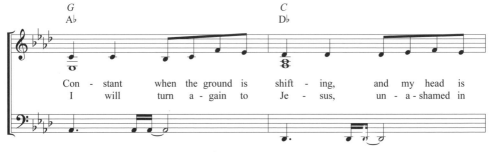

Con - stant when the ground is shift-ing, and my head is
I will turn a-gain to Je - sus, un-a-shamed in

164

CCLI# 7028211

165

166

# 52

# WHEN YOUR SPIRIT RUSHES IN
## [IN YOUR PRESENCE]

Key = E♭

Capo 1 (D)

Sarah Reeves & Jacob Sooter

o - cean, and we stand a - mazed, in your glo - ry.—— Chains and pri - son doors are bro - ken, where your free - dom reigns, in your pre - sence.—— 3. In the pre - sence.—— In your pre - sence.—— In your pre - sence. This—— room is a - live in your ma - je - sty; our——

*Last time to Coda*

*D.S. al Coda*

*Bridge*

168

ci - ty re - vived in your mer - cy.___ Your Son glo - ri - fied, our___

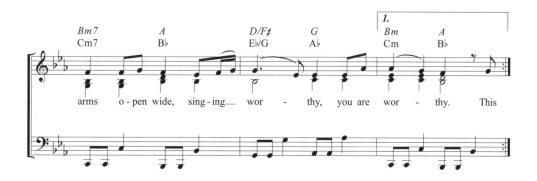

arms o - pen wide, sing - ing___ wor - thy, you are wor - thy. This

wor - thy, you are wor - thy, you are wor - thy. In your

pre - sence.___ In your pre - sence.

# 53

# WHERE CAN WE GO
## [CLING TO THE CROSS]

Key = A

Cathy Burton

Capo 2 (G)

1. Where can we go to find for-give-ness?
2. There on the cross he died to save us,
3. Where can we go to find the an-swers?

Where can we go with the bur-dens of life? We
There on the cross he dit it all; he
Where can we go with a ques-tion-ing heart?

look to the cross, where our Sa-viour longs to meet us, he
rose from the dead so that we can know for-give-ness, that
Who can we trust, when there's no one to list-en?

of-fers his love and sa-cri-fice.

171

# 54

# YOU ARE MATCHLESS IN GRACE AND MERCY
## [GOD WITH US]

Key = B

Bryan Torwalt
& Katie Torwalt

Capo 4 (G)

♩ = 72

1.You are match-less in grace_____ and mer-cy. There is
heal-er of the sick_____ and the bro-ken. You are
heart, it moves with com-pas - sion. There is

no-where we can hide_____ from your_____ love. You are
com - fort_____ for ev - 'ry heart that_____ mourns. Our_____
life, there is heal-ing in_____ your_____ love._____ You're the

stead - fast, ne-ver fail - ing._____ You are faith - ful. All cre -
King and our Sa - viour, for - e - ver. For e -
Fa - ther, the Son,_____ the Ho - ly_____ Spi - rit. And for e -

v3. Jump to ⊕

CCLI# 7054539

**1.**

Em / G#m    C / E    G / B

a - tion is in awe — of who — you are._____    2. You're the
ter - ni - ty,___ we will sing___ of all___ you've done.

**2.**    ⊕ (v.3)

G / B    Em / G#m    C / E

For e - ter - ni - ty,_____    we will sing    of all___ you've done.__
ter - ni - ty,_____    we will sing of all_____ you've done.

G / B    **Chorus**    𝄋 G / B (Last time 8vb)    C / E

We sing:    God with us,    God for us,

Em / G#m    C / E    (Fine)

no - thing could come a - gainst,    no one can stand be - tween___ us.

175

176

and you're lift - ing me___ up,     and you're lift - ing me___ up.___

*1.,2.*     *3.*

— When there was ___     and you're lift - ing me___ up,

and you're lift - ing me___ up.___     and you're lift - ing me___ up,

*D.S. al fine*

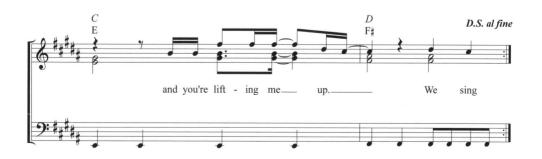

and you're lift - ing me___ up.___     We sing

# 55

# YOU ARE MY REFUGE
## [REFUGE]

Key = F

Cathy Burton

Capo 3 (D)

♩ = 96  **Verse**

1. You are my re-fuge, you are my strength, you're e-ver pre-sent
   You see me fal-ter, you see me fall, you ne-ver leave me,
2. Your word has spo-ken and I have heard; your love is stead-fast,
   I wait in si-lence for you a-lone; you're my sal-va-tion,

in ev-'ry-thing. And I will walk with you,— I will walk with you.
I can stand tall. And I will walk with you,— I will walk
your love is sure, and I be-long to you, I be-long to you.
you are my home and I be-long with you, I be-long

with you. I will be still and know that you are:

**Chorus**

(1.,3.,6.) — ex-al-ted in— the hea-vens, ex-al-ted on— the earth;—
(2.,4.,5.) — Our God can-not be sha-ken, our for-tress, safe— and true;—

CCLI# 5834606

179

180

# 56

# YOU CALLED OUT
## [NEVER GONNA STOP SINGING]

Key = F

Capo 3 (D)

♩ = 72

Ran Jackson,
Matt Vaughan & Tom Smith

*Verse*

You called out into darkness; you reached down
no longer bound in chains; you rescued me,

to save us.
and called me by name.

*Pre-Chorus*

You conquered the grave, your crossed the divide, lost in our sin, you made us a-

CCLI# 7054533

live.    How can we e - ver hold it in - side?    We can't hold back,

*Chorus*

we're gon - na lift you    High - er, high - er,

hearts burn - ing bright like a fi - re, fi - re.    Voi - ces u - nite, make it

loud - er, loud - er.    We're ne - ver gon - na stop sing - ing.    (Oh,)

*1.*
We're ne - ver gon - na stop sing - ing.

182

# 57

# YOU GIVE ME A BRAND NEW NAME
## [HELD HIGH]

Key = B

Capo 4 (G)

Sam Bailey & Nick Herbert

♪ = 156

**Verse**

1. You give me a brand new name, straight from your mouth oh— God.
   Fa - ther's love; dressed in your ro - yal— blood.
3. You've set my heart a - blaze with your sal - va - tion—flames.

you call me your pre - cious love, my fear and shame— are gone.
My heart for - e - ver safe, here in your grip— of grace.
Ris - ing with ho - ly light, know - ing I'm your de - light.

**1.**

Yes, I am yours; yes, I am yours. 2. Crowned with my

CCLI# 7043835

see my Fa - ther run    to hold me— a - gain.    My heart is o - ver-

come;    I'm cho - sen— by— grace.    I grace.

held high,    held    in your    hands.——————

My heart for - e - ver safe,    here in your    grip of grace.

186

TO THE ONE WHO IS VICTORIOUS...

I WILL GIVE THAT PERSON A WHITE STONE

WITH A NEW NAME WRITTEN ON IT,

KNOWN ONLY TO THE ONE WHO RECEIVES IT.

REVELATION 2:17

# 58

# YOU SIT ENTHRONED IN MAJESTY
## [ALL HAIL KING JESUS]

Key = C

Lou Fellingham, Nathan Fellingham
& Nick Herbert

CCLI# 7028218

migh - ty     for - e - ver - more.     You com - mand    my    breath,    call - ing

out    my    song.    Ho - ly___    ho    -    ly,    you are___    ho    -    ly    Lord of___

*Last time to Coda* ⊕ | **1st time only** | **1.**

___ all._____

**2.** | *D.C.* | **3.** | *D.S.*

You    sit    en -              All_____

⊕ *Coda*

# 59

# YOU UNRAVEL ME WITH A MELODY
## [NO LONGER SLAVES]

Key = B♭

Capo 3 (G)

♩ = 74

Brian Johnson,
Jonathan David Helser & Joel Case

(v.2)

*Verse*

G
B♭

Bm
Dm

1. You un-ra - vel me       with a me - lo - dy,       you sur-round
   — womb,       you have cho - sen me,       love

C
E♭

D
F

G
B♭

— me with— a song       of de-li-ve-rance       from my e-ne-
— has called— my name       I've been born— a-gain,       in-to your fa-

Bm
Dm

C
E♭

D
F

G
B♭

*Chorus*

- mies       till all— my fears— are gone.       I'm no long-
- mi-ly,       your blood— flows through       my veins.—

CCLI# 7030123

191

You split the sea, so I could walk right through it;
all my fears were drowned in per-fect love.
You res-cued me and I— will stand— and— sing: I am—
a child— of God.— I'm no long-

# YOUR NAME IS HONEY ON MY LIPS
## [HONEY]

Key = D

Trent

CCLI# 7029487

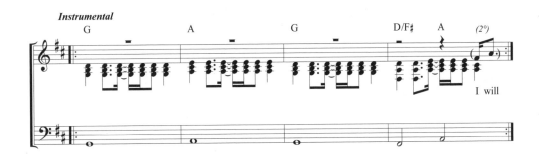

**Instrumental**

G             A            G          D/F♯  A    *(2°)*

I will

**Bridge**

G                              A

sing,    sing,    sing,      sing   a   new—   song,            a

*1.-3.*
D/F♯           A                *4.*
G                                           D/F♯

hymn   of    praise    to my— God.           I will    — God.

A                                                D

# BRIDGES TO C

# BRIDGES TO D

From F

From G

From B♭

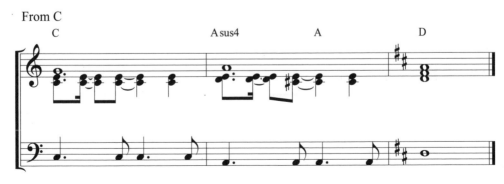

From C

# BRIDGES TO E

From G

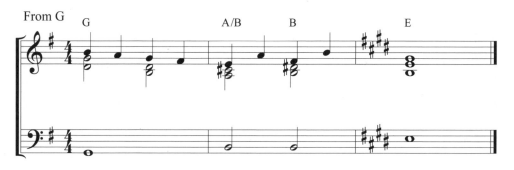

From A

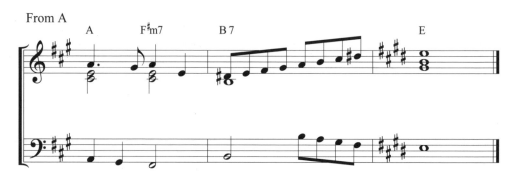

From C

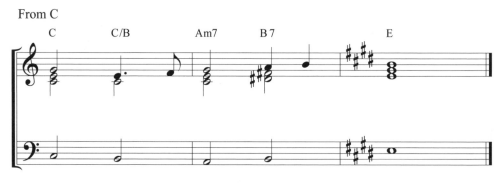

From D

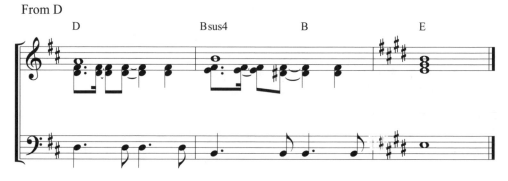

# BRIDGES TO F

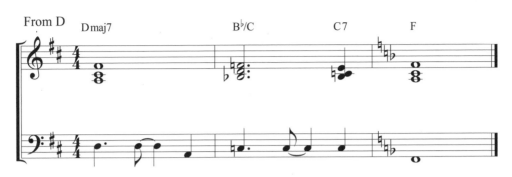

From D

Dmaj7       B♭/C       C7       F

From G

G       Csus4       C7       F

From B♭

B♭       Gm7       Csus4       C       F

From C

C   C/B   Am       Gm       C7       F

# BRIDGES TO G

# GUITAR CHORDS

A good chord vocabulary is essential for a guitarist to feel confident when playing in worship, especially when the situation may involve reading a previously unseen piece of music or picking up a song quickly by ear. The chords on these pages are arranged in 'families' according to key.

This is a beneficial way of remembering chords as most songs stick to these groupings. For each key, the first row shows the simplest form of each chord and the second line gives a more interesting substitution. The third line shows the chords most commonly used by guitarists derived by keeping some sort of pedal tone ringing in each chord and the fourth line shows inverted chords with an alternate bass note.

Also included are the Roman Numerals and Nashville Numbers associated with each chord. If you've not come across these before, they are simply an easy way of numbering each chord within a key. This is useful as it means you can take any chord progression in one key and instantly transpose it to another. Furthermore you can try out any of the chords in each column that corresponds to the relevant Roman Numeral and see if there is chord type or inversion which still fits but adds a different flavour. Experimentation like this may open up creative chord progressions that serve as a catalyst to help you to worship in fresh ways or to write new songs.

| | Roman | I | II | III | IV | V | VI | VII |
|---|---|---|---|---|---|---|---|---|
| | Nashville | 1 | 2 | 3 | 4 | 5 | 6 | 7 |
| Key of C | 3-note chord (triad) | C | Dm | Em | F | G | Am | Bdim |
| | 4-note chord | C maj7 | D m7 | E m7 | F maj7 | G7 | A m7 | B m7♭5 |
| | Alternative substitute | C | D7sus4 | Em7 | F sus2 | G5 | A m7 | Dsus4/B |
| | Alternative bass note | C/E | Dm/F | Em/G | F/A | F/G | Am/E | |

For all chords in the key of C# or Db, use the chords from the key of C with capo 1

# GUITAR CHORDS

| Roman | I | II | III | IV | V | VI | VII |
|---|---|---|---|---|---|---|---|
| Nashville | 1 | 2 | 3 | 4 | 5 | 6 | 7 |
| **Key of D** — 3-note chord (triad) | D | Em | F#m | G | A | Bm | C#dim |
| 4-note chord | Dmaj7 | Em7 | F#m7 | Gmaj7 | A7 | Bm7 | C#m7♭5 |
| Alternative substitute | Dsus2 | Em9 | F#m7 | G6sus2 | A7sus4 | Bm11 | Aadd9/C# |
| Alternative bass note | D/F# | Em/B | F#m/A | G/B | G/A | Bm/F# | |

For all chords in the key of D# or E♭, use the chords from the key of D with capo 1

| | | | | | | | |
|---|---|---|---|---|---|---|---|
| **Key of E** — 3-note chord (triad) | E | F#m | G#m | A | B | C#m | D#dim |
| 4-note chord | Emaj7 | F#m7 | G#m7 | Amaj7 | B7 | C#m7 | D#m7♭5 |
| Alternative substitute | E5 | F#m11 | G#madd♭6 | Aadd9 | Badd4 | C#m7 | D#alt |
| Alternative bass note | E/G# | F#m/C# | G#m/D# | A/C# | A/B | C#m/G# | |

For all chords in the key of F, use the chords from the key of E with capo 1

For all chords in the key of F# or Gb, use the chords from the key of E with capo 2

# GUITAR CHORDS

| Roman | I | II | III | IV | V | VI | VII |
|---|---|---|---|---|---|---|---|
| Nashville | 1 | 2 | 3 | 4 | 5 | 6 | 7 |

**Key of G**

| | I | II | III | IV | V | VI | VII |
|---|---|---|---|---|---|---|---|
| 3-note chord (triad) | G | Am | Bm | C | D | Em | F♯dim |
| 4-note chord | Gmaj7 | Am7 | Bm7 | Cmaj7 | D7 | Em7 | F♯m7♭5 |
| Alternative substitute | G | A7sus4 | Dsus4/B | Cadd9 | Dsus4 | Em7 | G/F♯ |
| Alternative bass note | G/D | Am/C | Bm/D | C/G | C/D | Em/G | |

For all chords in the key of G♯ or A♭, use the chords from the key of G with capo 1

**Key of A**

| | I | II | III | IV | V | VI | VII |
|---|---|---|---|---|---|---|---|
| 3-note chord (Triad) | A | Bm | C♯m | D | E | F♯m | G♯dim |
| 4-note chord | Amaj7 | Bm7 | C♯m7 | Dmaj7 | E7 | F♯m7 | G♯m7♭5 |
| Alternative substitute | Asus2 | Bsus4 | C♯m7 | D6sus2 | Eadd9 | F♯m11 | Eadd9/G♯ |
| Alternative bass note | A/E | Bm/F♯ | C♯m/E | D/A | D/E | F♯m/A | |

For all chords in the key of A♯ or Bb, use the chords from the key of A with capo 1

For all chords in the key of B, use the chords from the key of A with capo 2

# SCRIPTURE INDEX

## GENESIS

| | |
|---|---|
| 28:15 | From the breaking of the daylight |
| 31:27 | You unravel me with a melody |
| 32:11 | When my fears are overtaking |

## EXODUS

| | |
|---|---|
| 14:21 | God, you can tell the waves 'be still' |
| 15:2 | Let the King of my heart |

## LEVITICUS

| | |
|---|---|
| 26:30 | What fortune lies beyond the stars |

## DEUTERONOMY

| | |
|---|---|
| 10:12 | Go in peace |
| 26:18 | This is a holy moment |
| 32:4 | I've heard a thousand stories of what they think you're like |
| 32:4 | Mighty in battle, perfect in love |
| 34:4 | I can see the Promised Land |

## 2 SAMUEL

| | |
|---|---|
| 21:17 | I can see the Promised Land |
| 22:4 | You unravel me with a melody |
| 22:18 | You unravel me with a melody |

## 1 KINGS

| | |
|---|---|
| 11:36 | You unravel me with a melody |

## 2 KINGS

| | |
|---|---|
| 13:17 | You unravel me with a melody |

## 1 CHRONICLES

| | |
|---|---|
| 5:20 | Overwhelmed but I won't break |
| 17:20 | Immortal, invisible |

## 2 CHRONICLES

| | |
|---|---|
| 14:11 | Immortal, invisible |
| 20:21 | No eye has seen |

## JOB

| | |
|---|---|
| 9:5 | Hear our cry, oh King of heaven |
| 11:13-15 | Humbly I stand, an offering |
| 19:25 | What a Saviour |
| 22:26 | Overwhelmed but I won't break |
| 33:24 | Let the King of my heart |
| 35:5 | Immortal, invisible |
| 38:4 | What fortune lies beyond the stars |

## PSALMS

| | |
|---|---|
| 4:1 | When I call |
| 4:8 | When I call |
| 4:8 | You give me a brand new name |
| 5:11 | You called out |
| 7:1 | How sweet the sound of Jesus' name |
| 12:6 | Jesus, Jesus, how I trust you |
| 16:7 | My soul longs for Jesus |
| 16:8 | When my fears are overtaking |
| 16:11 | Watching, waiting for your fire again |
| 17:11 | You unravel me with a melody |
| 18:2 | You unravel me with a melody |
| 18:3 | You unravel me with a melody |
| 18:46 | All glory, all honour |
| 18:48 | You unravel me with a melody |
| 19:10 | Your name is honey on my lips |
| 19:14 | What a Saviour |
| 22:3 | You sit enthroned in majesty |
| 23:2-4 | Every painful day I've known |
| 23:3 | Your name is honey on my lips |
| 23:4 | For we trust in our God |
| 23:4 | When darkness deepens |
| 23:6 | Immortal, invisible |
| 24:8 | Mighty in battle, perfect in love |
| 26:12 | When darkness deepens |
| 27:1 | The Lord is our salvation |
| 27:1 | You give me a brand new name |
| 27:3 | For we trust in our God |
| 27:8 | I look upon the face |
| 27:14 | I will wait on you Lord |
| 28:7 | Jesus, Jesus, how I trust you |
| 29:2 | I look upon the face |
| 29:10 | Overhead, skies are dark |
| 29:10 | You sit enthroned in majesty |
| 30:5 | Our scars are a sign |
| 31:5 | You sit enthroned in majesty |
| 32:7 | You unravel me with a melody |
| 33:3 | Your name is honey on my lips |
| 34:4 | You unravel me with a melody |
| 34:5 | Jesus, Jesus, how I trust you |
| 35:10 | Before the earth was made you were living |
| 36:6 | Immortal, invisible |
| 36:9 | Let the King of my heart |
| 36:9 | You are matchless in grace and mercy |
| 37:3 | From the breaking of the daylight |
| 37:34 | I will wait on you Lord |
| 39:7 | All I am for you, oh Lord |
| 39:7 | When my fears are overtaking |
| 40:2 | I've come here today to worship again |
| 41:12 | Watching, waiting for your fire again |
| 42:1 | My soul longs for Jesus |
| 46:2 | For we trust in our God |
| 46:2 | Grander earth has quaked before |
| 46:7 | You are my refuge |
| 51:14 | Wake up my soul and turn to him |
| 54:10 | Overwhelmed but I won't break |
| 56:4 | Overwhelmed but I won't break |
| 56:13 | I was nowhere |

| | |
|---|---|
| 57:5 | Watching, waiting for your fire again |
| 57:8 | Wake up my soul and turn to him |
| 59:16 | God, you can tell the waves 'be still' |
| 61:1 | Hear our cry, oh King of heaven |
| 61:1-8 | Standing in this place of tears |
| 61:2 | Overwhelmed but I won't break |
| 62:5 | All I am for you, oh Lord |
| 62:5 | Grander earth has quaked before |
| 62:5 | Our scars are a sign |
| 62:5 | When my fears are overtaking |
| 62:5-6 | For we trust in our God |
| 62:6 | Overwhelmed but I won't break |
| 62:6-7 | The Lord is our salvation |
| 62:7 | You are my refuge |
| 62:8 | Overwhelmed but I won't break |
| 63:1 | My soul longs for Jesus |
| 65:1 | Humbly I stand, an offering |
| 69:9 | I'll be the altar |
| 72:26 | Let the King of my heart |
| 73:28 | When darkness deepens |
| 77:6 | My soul longs for Jesus |
| 77:14 | Let faith arise in spite of what I see |
| 81:7 | When my fears are overtaking |
| 84:2 | My soul longs for Jesus |
| 86:2 | Jesus, Jesus, how I trust you |
| 86:12 | Praise unbroken |
| 89:1 | Every painful day I've known |
| 89:1 | I will wait on you Lord |
| 89:13 | The Lord is our salvation |
| 89:16 | We are waiting |
| 90:2 | Before the earth was made you were living |
| 91:2 | The Lord is our salvation |
| 91:2 | You are my refuge |
| 93:1 | How sweet the sound of Jesus' name |
| 94:22 | You are my refuge |
| 95:2 | I've come here today to worship again |
| 95:2 | Praise unbroken |
| 95:6 | Where can we go |
| 96:1 | Your name is honey on my lips |
| 96:8 | I look upon the face |
| 97:5 | When your Spirit rushes in |
| 98:1 | Your name is honey on my lips |
| 99:3 | Mighty in battle, perfect in love |
| 100:2 | I've come here today to worship again |
| 100:5 | Every painful day I've known |
| 100:5 | Our scars are a sign |
| 102:1 | Hear our cry, oh King of heaven |
| 102:1 | Standing in this place of tears |
| 105:4 | I look upon the face |
| 108:1 | Wake up my soul and turn to him |
| 108:5 | Watching, waiting for your fire again |
| 108:5 | You are my refuge |
| 111:1 | Hear our cry, oh King of heaven |
| 112:4 | My soul longs for Jesus |
| 113:1 | Hear our cry, oh King of heaven |
| 115:9 | From the breaking of the daylight |
| 117:1 | Hear our cry, oh King of heaven |
| 117:2 | Our scars are a sign |
| 118:14 | Let the King of my heart |
| 119:43 | When my fears are overtaking |
| 119:73 | No eye has seen |
| 119:94 | You give me a brand new name |
| 119:103 | How sweet the sound of Jesus' name |
| 119:103 | Your name is honey on my lips |
| 119:105 | My soul longs for Jesus |
| 119:105 | Your name is honey on my lips |
| 119:111 | Let the King of my heart |
| 119:154 | Overhead, skies are dark |
| 119:159 | We are waiting |
| 121:1 | I've come here today to worship again |
| 123:1 | I've come here today to worship again |
| 126:4 | All glory, all honour |
| 130:2 | Hear our cry, oh King of heaven |
| 130:2 | Standing in this place of tears |
| 136:1 | Every painful day I've known |
| 136:1 | Overhead, skies are dark |
| 136:1 | You are matchless in grace and mercy |
| 138:2 | I look upon the face |
| 139:1 | Empty handed here I come |
| 139:7 | Where can we go |
| 139:7 | You are matchless in grace and mercy |
| 139:13 | You unravel me with a melody |
| 140:6 | Standing in this place of tears |
| 142:3 | Overwhelmed but I won't break |
| 142:5 | You are my refuge |
| 143:6 | My soul longs for Jesus |
| 144:2 | Overhead, skies are dark |
| 145:3 | Humbly I stand, an offering |
| 145:7 | You are matchless in grace and mercy |
| 145:10 | No eye has seen |
| 145:13 | Jesus, Jesus, how I trust you |
| 145:17 | I've heard a thousand stories of what they think you're like |
| 145:18 | When darkness deepens |
| 146:2 | God, you can tell the waves 'be still' |
| 146:6 | Our God is a keeper of his word |
| 147:1 | Hear our cry, oh King of heaven |
| 147:3 | All I am for you, oh Lord |
| 148:5 | I cast my mind to Calvary |
| 148:13 | No eye has seen |
| 149:1 | Your name is honey on my lips |

## PROVERBS

| | |
|---|---|
| 20:22 | I will wait on you Lord |

## SONG OF SONGS

| | |
|---|---|
| 4:11 | Your name is honey on my lips |

## ISAIAH

| | |
|---|---|
| 6:3 | You sit enthroned in majesty |
| 7:14 | Jesus Christ, Emmanuel |
| 12:2 | All glory, all honour |
| 12:6 | You called out |
| 26:4 | From the breaking of the daylight |
| 30:29 | God, you can tell the waves 'be still' |
| 35:6 | All glory, all honour |
| 35:7 | My soul longs for Jesus |
| 37:16 | You sit enthroned in majesty |
| 40:5 | This is a holy moment |
| 40:7 | Immortal, invisible |
| 40:29 | From him, through him, and to him are all things |
| 42:5 | No eye has seen |
| 42:10 | Your name is honey on my lips |
| 43:1-2 | Overhead, skies are dark |
| 45:23 | Where can we go |
| 49:7 | Our God is a keeper of his word |
| 50:7 | Let the King of my heart |
| 51:6 | No eye has seen |
| 55:9 | No eye has seen |
| 58:10 | You called out |
| 60:1 | This is a holy moment |
| 61:1 | You are matchless in grace and mercy |
| 61:3 | Standing in this place of tears |
| 62:2-4 | You give me a brand new name |
| 64:6 | No eye has seen |

## JEREMIAH

| | |
|---|---|
| 1:6-7 | You unravel me with a melody |
| 16:19 | You are my refuge |
| 17:7 | From the breaking of the daylight |
| 29:11 | From the breaking of the daylight |
| 31:3 | O love that will not let me go |
| 32:9 | What fortune lies beyond the stars |

## LAMENTATIONS

| | |
|---|---|
| 3:22-23 | My soul longs for Jesus |
| 3:22-23 | Overhead, skies are dark |
| 3:23 | Every painful day I've known |
| 3:24 | Our God is a keeper of his word |
| 3:32 | You give me a brand new name |

## EZEKIEL

| | |
|---|---|
| 11:19 | How sweet the sound of Jesus' name |
| 34:16 | When I was lost |
| 36:26 | How sweet the sound of Jesus' name |
| 37:5 | Spirit of God |

## DANIEL

| | |
|---|---|
| 2:47 | From him, through him, and to him are all things |
| 7:9 | Immortal, invisible |
| 7:13 | Immortal, invisible |
| 7:22 | Immortal, invisible |
| 9:3 | Our God is a keeper of his word |

## HOSEA

| | |
|---|---|
| 6:1 | We are waiting |
| 13:4 | You called out |

## JONAH

| | |
|---|---|
| 2:9 | Wake up my soul and turn to him |

## MICAH

| | |
|---|---|
| 7:16 | We all stand amazed |

## HABAKKUK

| | |
|---|---|
| 3:9 | You unravel me with a melody |

## MATTHEW

| | |
|---|---|
| 1:23 | Jesus Christ, Emmanuel |
| 4:17 | What fortune lies beyond the stars |
| 7:7-12 | I've heard a thousand stories of what they think you're like |
| 11:19 | What a Saviour |
| 11:29 | You are my refuge |
| 16:3 | Overhead, skies are dark |
| 18:6 | You unravel me with a melody |
| 18:11 | When I was lost |
| 19:26 | I can see the Promised Land |
| 19:26 | Let faith arise in spite of what I see |
| 26:36 | I have a home |
| 26:48 | Jesus Christ, Emmanuel |
| 27:60 | Jesus Christ, Emmanuel |

## MARK

| | |
|---|---|
| 4:35-41 | God, you can tell the waves 'be still' |
| 5:13 | You unravel me with a melody |
| 5:34 | Go in peace |
| 9:24 | Let faith arise in spite of what I see |
| 10:27 | Let faith arise in spite of what I see |
| 14:32 | I have a home |
| 14:44 | Jesus Christ, Emmanuel |

## LUKE

| | |
|---|---|
| 1:37 | I can see the Promised Land |
| 1:47 | What a Saviour |
| 4:18 | You are matchless in grace and mercy |
| 4:36 | Watching, waiting for your fire again |
| 7:34 | What a Saviour |
| 7:50 | Go in peace |
| 8:48 | Go in peace |
| 18:27 | Let faith arise in spite of what I see |
| 22:47 | Jesus Christ, Emmanuel |
| 23:33 | I cast my mind to Calvary |

## JOHN

| | |
|---|---|
| 1:1 | Before the earth was made you were living |
| 1:5 | I was nowhere |
| 1:5 | You called out |
| 1:10 | Our God is a keeper of his word |
| 1:29 | How sweet the sound of Jesus' name |
| 1:36 | How sweet the sound of Jesus' name |
| 2:17 | I'll be the altar |
| 3:3 | My soul longs for Jesus |
| 9:25 | I was nowhere |
| 10:7 | When I was lost |
| 11:27 | Every painful day I've known |
| 12:46 | Hear our cry, oh King of heaven |
| 14:6 | I was nowhere |
| 14:16 | I have a home |
| 14:16-17 | Spirit of God |
| 14:26 | Spirit of God |
| 14:27 | When my fears are overtaking |
| 15:7 | I have a home |
| 15:13 | When your Spirit rushes in |
| 15:26 | Spirit of God |
| 20:22 | Spirit of God |

## ACTS

| | |
|---|---|
| 2:2 | When your Spirit rushes in |
| 2:2-5 | Watching, waiting for your fire again |
| 2:25 | Overwhelmed but I won't break |
| 2:17-18 | Our God is a keeper of his word |
| 4:12 | Wake up my soul and turn to him |
| 12:7 | When your Spirit rushes in |
| 16:16-40 | God, you can tell the waves 'be still' |
| 16:26 | When your Spirit rushes in |
| 17:25 | Immortal, invisible |

## ROMANS

| | |
|---|---|
| 5:2 | When I was lost |
| 5:8 | I cast my mind to Calvary |
| 5:17 | We all stand amazed |
| 8:18-19 | This is a holy moment |
| 8:21 | When your Spirit rushes in |
| 8:31 | For we trust in our God |
| 8:35 | O love that will not let me go |
| 8:38 | Empty handed here I come |

| 8:38 | You are matchless in grace and mercy |
| 8:38-39 | I will wait on you Lord |
| 10:9 | Where can we go |
| 11:6 | When I was lost |
| 11:36 | From him, through him, and to him are all things |
| 12:1 | Humbly I stand, an offering |
| 12:1 | I'll be the altar |
| 14:11 | We all stand amazed |
| 14:11 | Where can we go |
| 15:7 | I'll be the altar |
| 16:27 | Immortal, invisible |

## 1 CORINTHIANS

| 2:9 | No eye has seen |
| 2:12 | When I was lost |
| 3:17 | Spirit of God |
| 3:18 | This is a holy moment |
| 4:7 | Jesus, Jesus, how I trust you |
| 5:14 | O love that will not let me go |
| 7:24 | I have a home |
| 10:31 | All I am for you, oh Lord |
| 12:9 | Overwhelmed but I won't break |
| 13:2 | I can see the Promised Land |
| 13:12 | When darkness deepens |
| 15:51 | No eye has seen |
| 15:52 | We all stand amazed |
| 15:54 | When I was lost |
| 15:55 | All glory, all honour |

## GALATIANS

| 2:9 | When I was lost |
| 3:13 | I've come here today to worship again |
| 4:7 | You unravel me with a melody |

## EPHESIANS

| 1:6 | We all stand amazed |
| 1:6 | What a Saviour |
| 1:7 | I've come here today to worship again |
| 2:4 | You give me a brand new name |
| 2:7 | We all stand amazed |
| 2:7 | What a Saviour |
| 3:14-21 | What fortune lies beyond the stars |
| 4:2 | Humbly I stand, an offering |

## PHILIPPIANS

| 1:11 | I'll be the altar |
| 1:19 | You give me a brand new name |
| 2:3 | Humbly I stand, an offering |
| 2:7-9 | Before the earth was made you were living |
| 2:9 | For we trust in our God |
| 2:9 | How sweet the sound of Jesus' name |
| 2:9 | I can see the Promised Land |
| 2:9 | My soul longs for Jesus |
| 2:10 | You called out |
| 2:11 | We all stand amazed |
| 2:11 | Where can we go |
| 2:16 | How sweet the sound of Jesus' name |

## COLOSSIANS

| 1:13 | I was nowhere |
| 1:13 | You called out |
| 3:2 | Grander earth has quaked before |
| 3:5 | All I am for you, oh Lord |
| 3:12 | Humbly I stand, an offering |

## 1 TIMOTHY

| 1:17 | Immortal, invisible |

## 2 TIMOTHY

| 1:10 | No eye has seen |

## TITUS

| 2:13 | All glory, all honour |
| 2:13 | This is a holy moment |
| 2:13 | We are waiting |
| 3:4 | What a Saviour |

## HEBREWS

| 1:3 | We all stand amazed |
| 2:9 | Mighty in battle, perfect in love |
| 2:12 | I've come here today to worship again |
| 2:14 | How sweet the sound of Jesus' name |
| 6:19 | Let the King of my heart |
| 6:19 | We are waiting |
| 10:2 | We all stand amazed |
| 12:2 | Grander earth has quaked before |
| 12:2 | Jesus, Jesus, how I trust you |
| 12:11 | Every painful day I've known |
| 12:12 | What fortune lies beyond the stars |
| 12:28 | Let faith arise in spite of what I see |
| 13:5 | Go in peace |
| 13:5 | You are my refuge |
| 13:8 | We are waiting |

## JAMES

| 1:2 | I look upon the face |
| 4:6 | We all stand amazed |
| 4:6 | What a Saviour |
| 4:8 | I have a home |
| 4:10 | Our God is a keeper of his word |
| 4:12 | Humbly I stand, an offering |

## 1 PETER

| 1:7 | I look upon the face |
| 1:18 | How sweet the sound of Jesus' name |
| 1:18 | I've come here today to worship again |
| 1:18 | When I was lost |
| 1:23 | My soul longs for Jesus |
| 1:23 | You unravel me with a melody |
| 5:6 | Humbly I stand, an offering |
| 5:6 | Our God is a keeper of his word |
| 5:10 | When I was lost |

## 1 JOHN

| 1:1 | Before the earth was made you were living |
| 1:1 | How sweet the sound of Jesus' name |
| 3:10 | You unravel me with a melody |
| 4:4 | From him, through him, and to him are all things |
| 4:10 | I've come here today to worship again |
| 4:14 | What a Saviour |

## 2 JOHN

| 1:3 | Empty handed here I come |

## 3 JOHN

| | |
|---|---|
| 2:2 | Grander earth has quaked before |
| 2:2 | Our scars are a sign |

## JUDE

| | |
|---|---|
| 1:1 | I've heard a thousand stories of what they think you're like |
| 1:24 | The Lord is our salvation |
| 1:25 | All glory, all honour |
| 1:25 | Praise unbroken |

## REVELATION

| | |
|---|---|
| 1:4 | From him, through him, and to him are all things |
| 2:17 | You give me a brand new name |
| 3:4 | I will wait on you Lord |
| 4:8 | From him, through him, and to him are all things |
| 4:8 | You sit enthroned in majesty |
| 4:11 | Mighty in battle, perfect in love |
| 4:11 | The Lord is our salvation |
| 4:11 | When your Spirit rushes in |
| 4:11 | You sit enthroned in majesty |
| 5:9 | You sit enthroned in majesty |
| 5:12 | Jesus Christ, Emmanuel |
| 5:12 | The Lord is our salvation |
| 5:12-13 | Wake up my soul and turn to him |
| 5:13 | All glory, all honour |
| 7:9 | I cast my mind to Calvary |
| 7:11 | Immortal, invisible |
| 7:12 | The Lord is our salvation |
| 7:17 | Empty handed here I come |
| 11:15 | From him, through him, and to him are all things |
| 17:14 | You called out |
| 19:1 | Jesus Christ, Emmanuel |
| 19:1 | Wake up my soul and turn to him |
| 19:4 | We are waiting |
| 19:6 | How sweet the sound of Jesus' name |
| 19:6 | When I was lost |
| 19:11 | Mighty in battle, perfect in love |
| 21:4 | Empty handed here I come |
| 21:6 | Let the King of my heart |
| 22:3 | When darkness deepens |
| 22:5 | From him, through him, and to him are all things |
| 22:20 | My soul longs for Jesus |

# THEMATIC INDEX

## CALL TO WORSHIP

From him, through him, and to him are all things

I've come here today to worship again

Mighty in battle, perfect in love

Praise unbroken

This is a holy moment

Wake up my soul and turn to him

What a Saviour

Where can we go

You called out

You sit enthroned in majesty

## THE CHURCH, THE PEOPLE OF GOD

For we trust in our God

Go in peace

The Lord is our salvation

We are waiting

You called out

## COME LORD JESUS - THE PRESENCE OF GOD

All glory, all honour

Hear our cry, oh King of heaven

I have a home

I've heard a thousand stories of what they think you're like

Lover of my soul

My soul longs for Jesus

Our God is a keeper of his word

Spirit of God

This is a holy moment

Watching, waiting for your fire again

When darkness deepens

When your Spirit rushes in

## COMMUNION (SEE ALSO JESUS - CROSS AND RESURRECTION)

I cast my mind to Calvary

Jesus Christ, Emmanuel

When I was lost

## CONFESSION

I was nowhere

I've come here today to worship again

What fortune lies beyond the stars

When I was lost

Where can we go

You give me a brand new name

Your name is honey on my lips

## CREATION

Before the earth was made you were living

No eye has seen

## DEDICATION AND COMMITMENT

All I am for you, oh Lord

Empty handed here I come

Humbly I stand, an offering

I will wait on you Lord

I'll be the altar

Lover of my soul

O love that will not let me go

Praise unbroken

Where can we go

You called out

## FAITH AND TRUST

Empty handed here I come

Every painful day I've known

For we trust in our God

From the breaking of the daylight

God, you can tell the waves 'be still'

Grander earth has quaked before

Jesus, Jesus, how I trust you

Humbly I stand, an offering

I look upon the face

Let faith arise in spite of what I see

Let the King of my heart

Our scars are a sign

Overhead, skies are dark

Overwhelmed but I won't break

Standing in this place of tears

The Lord is our salvation

We are waiting

When darkness deepens

When I call

When my fears are overtaking

You are my refuge

Your name is honey on my lips

## FAMILY WORSHIP

Go in peace

When I call

## GOD, LORD AND FATHER

Hear our cry, oh King of heaven

I've come here today to worship again

I've heard a thousand stories of what they think you're like

Standing in this place of tears

The Lord is our salvation

You are my refuge

You unravel me with a melody

## GOD'S LOVE AND FAITHFULNESS

Every painful day I've known

From the breaking of the daylight

God, you can tell the waves 'be still'

I can see the Promised Land

I have a home

I was nowhere

I will wait on you Lord

I've heard a thousand stories of what they think you're like

Let faith arise in spite of what I see

Let the King of my heart

Lover of my soul

O love that will not let me go

Our scars are a sign

Overhead, skies are dark

Overwhelmed but I won't break

Standing in this place of tears

When darkness deepens

When I was lost

When your Spirit rushes in

You are my refuge

You give me a brand new name

You unravel me with a melody

## GUIDANCE AND DIRECTION

From the breaking of the daylight
Jesus, Jesus, how I trust you
I will wait on you Lord
My soul longs for Jesus
Overwhelmed but I won't break
Spirit of God
Where can we go
Your name is honey on my lips

## HEALING

All glory, all honour
I have nothing left to give you
Standing in this place of tears
You are matchless in grace and mercy
You unravel me with a melody

## HEART WORSHIP

God, you can tell the waves 'be still'
Jesus, Jesus, how I trust you
How sweet the sound of Jesus' name
I look upon the face
I will wait on you Lord
I'll be the altar
I've come here today to worship again
Let the King of my heart
My soul longs for Jesus
No eye has seen
Praise unbroken
This is a holy moment
Wake up my soul and turn to him
What a Saviour
When my fears are overtaking
Where can we go
You are my refuge
You called out
You sit enthroned in majesty
You unravel me with a melody
Your name is honey on my lips

## HEAVEN AND THE PROMISE OF ETERNITY

Empty handed here I come
How sweet the sound of Jesus' name
I cast my mind to Calvary
I have a home
My soul longs for Jesus
When darkness deepens

## HOLY SPIRIT

Immortal, invisible
Our God is a keeper of his word
Spirit of God
Watching, waiting for your fire again
We are waiting
When your Spirit rushes in

## JESUS - CROSS AND RESURRECTION

Before the earth was made you were living
How sweet the sound of Jesus' name
I cast my mind to Calvary
Immortal, invisible
Jesus Christ, Emmanuel
We all stand amazed
What a Saviour
When I was lost
Where can we go

## LOVE AND DEVOTION

Empty handed here I come
God, you can tell the waves 'be still'
Jesus, Jesus, how I trust you
How sweet the sound of Jesus' name
I look upon the face
I will wait on you Lord
I'll be the altar
My soul longs for Jesus
Overwhelmed but I won't break
Praise unbroken
What a Saviour
You are my refuge
You called out
You sit enthroned in majesty
Your name is honey on my lips

## MERCY, GRACE AND FORGIVENESS

All glory, all honour
How sweet the sound of Jesus' name
I look upon the face
I was nowhere
Immortal, invisible
I've come here today to worship again
Overhead, skies are dark
Wake up my soul and turn to him
We all stand amazed
What a Saviour
What fortune lies beyond the stars
When I was lost
You are matchless in grace and mercy
You called out
You give me a brand new name

## MISSION

Spirit of God

## MYSTERY/ TRANSCENDENCE AND POWER OF GOD

Before the earth was made you were living
From him, through him, and to him are all things
Hear our cry, oh King of heaven
Immortal, invisible
Grander earth has quaked before
Let faith arise in spite of what I see
Mighty in battle, perfect in love
No eye has seen
The Lord is our salvation
When your Spirit rushes in
You sit enthroned in majesty

## PRAISE AND THANKSGIVING

Before the earth was made you were living
Hear our cry, oh King of heaven
How sweet the sound of Jesus' name
I cast my mind to Calvary
I look upon the face
Immortal, invisible
Jesus Christ, Emmanuel
Mighty in battle, perfect in love
Praise unbroken
This is a holy moment
Wake up my soul and turn to him
We all stand amazed
What a Saviour
You called out
Your name is honey on my lips

## PRAYER AND INTERCESSION

All glory, all honour
I have a home
I will wait on you Lord
Our God is a keeper of his word
We are waiting
What fortune lies beyond the stars
When darkness deepens
When I call
Where can we go
You are my refuge

## PROCLAMATION

Before the earth was made you were living

For we trust in our God

From him, through him, and to him are all things

I can see the Promised Land

I was nowhere

Mighty in battle, perfect in love

The Lord is our salvation

You are matchless in grace and mercy

You called out

You sit enthroned in majesty

## RENEWAL AND REFRESHMENT

God, you can tell the waves 'be still'

I've heard a thousand stories of what they think you're like

Let the King of my heart

Lover of my soul

My soul longs for Jesus

O love that will not let me go

Our scars are a sign

Overwhelmed but I won't break

Spirit of God

Watching, waiting for your fire again

When my fears are overtaking

When your Spirit rushes in

You are my refuge

You give me a brand new name

## RESPONSE

All I am for you, oh Lord

Every painful day I've known

For we trust in our God

From the breaking of the daylight

Go in peace

Grander earth has quaked before

Jesus, Jesus, how I trust you

Humbly I stand, an offering

I look upon the face

I will wait on you Lord

I'll be the altar

Let faith arise in spite of what I see

Our God is a keeper of his word

Our scars are a sign

Overwhelmed but I won't break

Spirit of God

We all stand amazed

When I was lost

Where can we go

You are my refuge

You called out

You unravel me with a melody

Your name is honey on my lips

## SPIRITUAL WARFARE

For we trust in our God

From him, through him, and to him are all things

Hear our cry, oh King of heaven

I can see the Promised Land

Let faith arise in spite of what I see

The Lord is our salvation

When my fears are overtaking

You are matchless in grace and mercy

You unravel me with a melody

## SUFFERING AND TRIALS

Empty handed here I come

Every painful day I've known

From the breaking of the daylight

God, you can tell the waves 'be still'

Grander earth has quaked before

Jesus, Jesus, how I trust you

I have a home

Let faith arise in spite of what I see

O love that will not let me go

Our scars are a sign

Overhead, skies are dark

Overwhelmed but I won't break

Standing in this place of tears

When darkness deepens

When I call

When my fears are overtaking

Where can we go

You are my refuge

## SUITABLE FOR SOLO OR PRESENTATION

Empty handed here I come

Every painful day I've known

Go in peace

Grander earth has quaked before

I'll be the altar

Lover of my soul

Overhead, skies are dark

Standing in this place of tears

What fortune lies beyond the stars

You unravel me with a melody

## TRINITY

You are matchless in grace and mercy